PRIMARY MATHEMATICS Standards Edition

TEXTBOOK

Marshall Cavendish Education

SingaporeMath.com Inc

Original edition published under the title Primary Mathematics Textbook 3B
© 1982 Curriculum Planning & Development Division, Ministry of Education, Singapore
Published by Times Media Private Limited

This edition © 2008 Marshall Cavendish International (Singapore) Private Limited

Published by Marshall Cavendish Education
An imprint of Marshall Cavendish
Marshall Cavendish is a trademark of Times Publishing Limited

Marshall Cavendish Corporation
99 White Plains Road
Tarrytown, NY 10591
U.S.A.
Tel: (1-914) 332 8888
Fax: (1-914) 332 8882
E-mail: mcc@marshallcavendish.com
Website: www.marshallcavendish.com

Distributed by
SingaporeMath.com Inc
404 Beavercreek Road #225
Oregon City, OR 97045
U.S.A.
Website: www.singaporemath.com

Marshall Cavendish International (Singapore) Private Limited
Times Centre, 1 New Industrial Road
Singapore 536196
Tel: +65 6411 0820
Fax: +65 6266 3677
E-mail: fps@sg.marshallcavendish.com
Website: www.marshallcavendish.com/education/sg

First published 2008

Primary Mathematics (Standards Edition) Textbook 3B
ISBN 978-0-7614-6982-7

Printed in Singapore

Primary Mathematics (Standards Edition) is adapted from Primary Mathematics Textbook 3B (3rd Edition), originally
developed by the Ministry of Education, Singapore. This edition contains new content developed by Marshall Cavendish
International (Singapore) Private Limited, which is not attributable to the Ministry of Education, Singapore.

We would like to acknowledge the Project Team from the Ministry of Education, Singapore, that developed the original
Singapore Edition:
Project Director: Dr Kho Tek Hong
Team Members: Hector Chee Kum Hoong, Chip Wai Lung, Liang Hin Hoon, Lim Eng Tann,
              Rosalind Lim Hui Cheng, Ng Hwee Wan, Ng Siew Lee
Curriculum Specialists: Christina Cheong Ngan Peng, Ho Juan Beng

Our thanks to Richard Askey, Emeritus Professor of Mathematics (University of Wisconsin, Madison) and Madge Goldman,
President (Gabriella and Paul Rosenbaum Foundation), for their help and advice in the production of Primary Mathematics
(Standards Edition).

We would also like to recognize the contributions of Jennifer Hoerst (Curriculum Advisor, SingaporeMath.com Inc) and
Bill Jackson (Math Coach, School No. 2, Paterson, New Jersey) to Primary Mathematics (Standards Edition).

PREFACE

PRIMARY MATHEMATICS (Standards Edition) is a complete program from the publishers of Singapore's successful *Primary Mathematics* series. Newly adapted to align with the Mathematics Framework for California Public Schools, the program aims to equip students with sound concept development, critical thinking and efficient problem-solving skills.

Mathematical concepts are introduced in the opening pages and taught to mastery through specific learning tasks that allow for immediate assessment and consolidation.

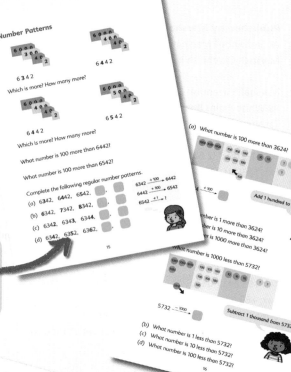

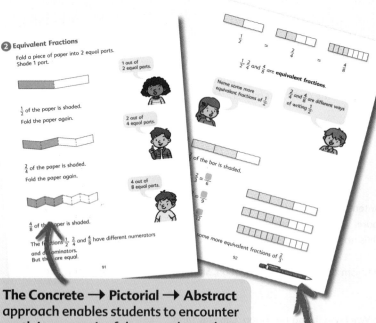

The **modeling method** enables students to visualize and solve mathematical problems quickly and efficiently.

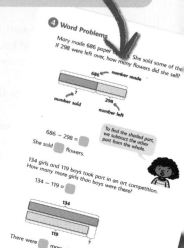

The Concrete → Pictorial → Abstract approach enables students to encounter math in a meaningful way and translate mathematical skills from the concrete to the abstract.

The **pencil icon** ✏️ Exercise 18, pages 18-20 ▷ provides quick and easy reference from the Textbook to the relevant Workbook pages. The **direct correlation** of the Workbook to the Textbook facilitates focused review and evaluation.

New mathematical concepts are introduced through a **spiral progression** that builds on concepts already taught and mastered.

Metacognition is employed as a strategy for learners to monitor their thinking processes in problem solving. Speech and thought bubbles provide guidance through the thought processes, making even the most challenging problems accessible to students.

The color patch ▢ is used to invite active student participation and to facilitate lively discussion about the mathematical concepts taught.

Regular **reviews** in the Textbook provide consolidation of concepts learnt.

The **glossary** effectively combines pictorial representation with simple mathematical definitions to provide a comprehensive reference guide for students.

CONTENTS

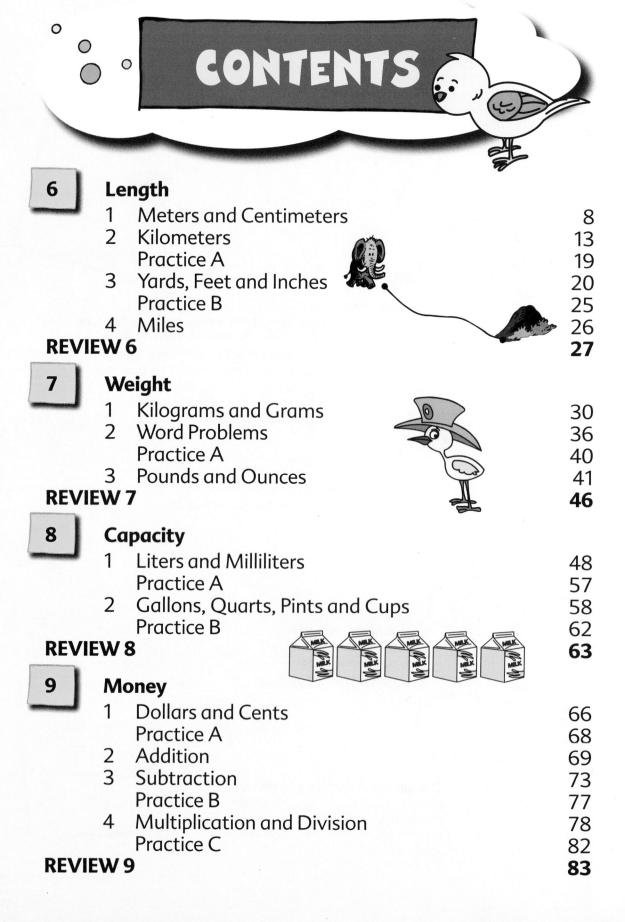

6 LENGTH

1 Meters and Centimeters

Get a meter ruler and find out how long 1 meter is.

Estimate the length of the board in the classroom.
Then check by measuring it with the meter ruler.

Is the length closer to 2 m or 3 m?

Estimate the height of the door in your classroom.
Check by measuring.

The **meter (m)** and **centimeter (cm)** are units of length.
1 m = 100 cm

1. Which of these tools would you use to measure
   (a) the width of a room
   (b) the size of your waist
   (c) the length and width of your math book
   (d) the width of a door?

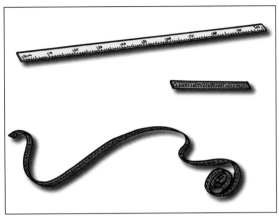

2. Would you use meters or centimeters to measure
   (a) the length of a playground
   (b) the length of a crayon
   (c) the length of a butterfly
   (d) the length of the hallway?

You can measure in meters and centimeters!

3. Joe's height is 1 m 25 cm.

   (a) 1 m 25 cm is ⬜ cm more than 1 m.

   (b) 1 m 25 cm = ⬜ cm

4. (a) Write 2 m in centimeters.

   2 m = ⬜ cm

   (b) Write 300 cm in meters.

   300 cm = ⬜ m

5. (a) Estimate the length of your classroom.
   Then measure the length in meters and centimeters.
   Write the distance in meters and centimeters.

   (b) Estimate how far you can walk in 5 steps.
   Then walk 5 steps and measure the distance in meters and centimeters.
   Write the distance in meters and centimeters.

6. David's long jump result is 1 m 45 cm.
   Write the distance in centimeters.

   1 m 45 cm = ⬜ cm

7. Write in centimeters.
   (a) 1 m 90 cm   (b) 1 m 55 cm   (c) 2 m 86 cm
   (d) 2 m 89 cm   (e) 3 m 8 cm   (f) 4 m 6 cm

8. A car is 395 cm long.   300 cm = 3 m
   Write the length in meters and centimeters.

   395 cm = ⬜ m ⬜ cm

9. Write in meters and centimeters.
   (a) 180 cm   (b) 195 cm   (c) 262 cm
   (d) 299 cm   (e) 304 cm   (f) 409 cm

10. The table shows the results of the shot put finals.

Name	Distance
Ryan	1 m 89 cm
Andy	2 m 8 cm
Tyrone	1 m 96 cm

Arrange the distances in order. Begin with the shortest.

Exercise 1, page 7

11. Find the value of 1 m − 35 cm.

100 cm − 35 cm = ☐

35 cm + ☐ = 100 cm

$$1\ m = 100\ cm$$
$$100 = 90 + 10$$

$$\begin{array}{r} 9\ \text{tens}\ 10\ \text{ones} \\ -\quad 3\ \text{tens}\ \ 5\ \text{ones} \\ \hline 6\ \text{tens}\ \ 5\ \text{ones} \end{array}$$

$$35 \xrightarrow{+5} 40 \xrightarrow{+60} 100$$
or
$$35 \xrightarrow{+60} 95 \xrightarrow{+5} 100$$

1 m − 35 cm = ☐ cm

$$3\ m − 2\ m = 1\ m$$
$$1\ m − 35\ cm = ☐\ cm$$

12. Find the value of 3 m − 2 m 35 cm.

3 m − 2 m 35 cm = ☐ cm

13. Find the missing numbers.

(a) 1 m − 40 cm = ☐ cm

(b) 1 m − 85 cm = ☐ cm

(c) 1 m − 43 cm = ☐ cm

(d) 1 m − 67 cm = ☐ cm

(e) 32 cm + ☐ cm = 1 m

(f) 91 cm + ☐ cm = 1 m

(g) 2 m − 1 m 25 cm = ☐ cm

(h) 3 m − 2 m 46 cm = ☐ cm

(i) 6 m − 5 m 4 cm = ☐ cm

(j) 9 m 73 cm + ☐ cm = 10 m

Exercise 2, page 8

14. Lily has a red ribbon 3 m 40 cm long and a yellow ribbon 1 m 85 cm long.

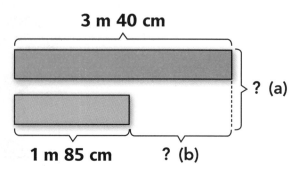

3 m 40 cm

? (a)

1 m 85 cm   ? (b)

(a) Find the total length of the ribbons.

3 m 40 cm + 1 m 85 cm = ⬜ m ⬜ cm

3 m 40 cm $\xrightarrow{+1\,m}$ 4 m 40 cm $\xrightarrow{+85\,cm}$ 5 m 25 cm

The total length of the ribbons is

⬜ m ⬜ cm.

(b) How much longer is the red ribbon than the yellow ribbon?

3 m 40 cm − 1 m 85 cm = ⬜ m ⬜ cm

3 m 40 cm $\xrightarrow{-1\,m}$ 2 m 40 cm $\xrightarrow{-85\,cm}$ 1 m 55 cm

The red ribbon is ⬜ m ⬜ cm longer than the yellow ribbon.

15. Add or subtract in compound units.
    (a) 4 m 32 cm + 5 m   (b) 3 m 65 cm + 14 cm
    (c) 7 m 85 cm + 45 cm   (d) 2 m 18 cm + 4 m 28 cm
    (e) 1 m 65 cm + 1 m 55 cm   (f) 6 m 28 cm + 2 m 73 cm
    (g) 9 m 15 cm − 3 m   (h) 5 m 39 cm − 15 cm
    (i) 5 m − 45 cm   (j) 6 m 15 cm − 2 m 20 cm
    (k) 4 m 35 cm − 80 cm   (l) 8 m 5 cm − 5 m 75 cm

Exercise 3, pages 9-10

2 Kilometers

The **kilometer (km)**, meter (m) and centimeter (cm) are units of length.

1 km = 1000 m
1 m = 100 cm

A bus is about 10 m long. The total length of 100 buses is about 1 km.

Airport 1 km

We measure long distances in kilometers.

1.

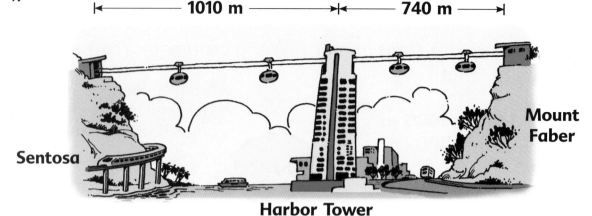

1010 m — 740 m

Sentosa

Mount Faber

Harbor Tower

(a) The distance between Sentosa and Harbor Tower
is ⬜ km ⬜ m.

(b) The distance between Mount Faber and Sentosa
is ⬜ km ⬜ m.

2.

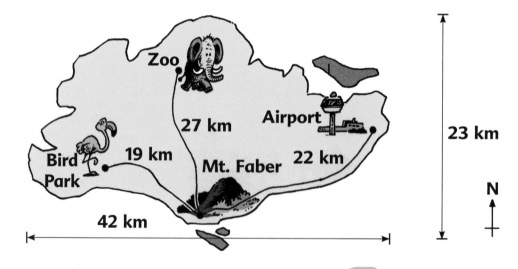

Zoo

27 km   Airport

Bird Park   19 km   Mt. Faber   22 km

42 km

23 km

N

(a) The distance across Singapore is about ⬜ km
from west to east.

It is about ⬜ km from north to south.

(b) The distance from the Bird Park to the airport
is about ⬜ km.

3.

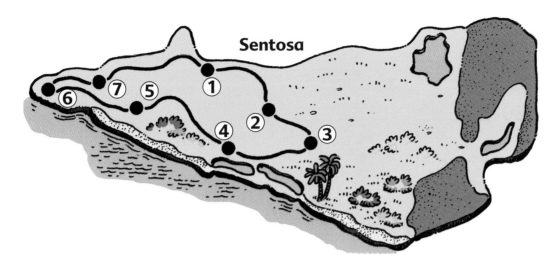

The total length of the train route on Sentosa Island is about 6 km 100 m.
Write the length in meters.

6 km = 6000 m

4. The distance around a running track is 400 m.
Ryan ran round the track 3 times.

He ran km m.

5. Write in meters.
   (a) 1 km 600 m   (b) 2 km 550 m   (c) 2 km 605 m
   (d) 3 km 85 m   (e) 3 km 20 m   (f) 4 km 5 m

6. Write in kilometers and meters.
   (a) 1830 m   (b) 2304 m   (c) 2780 m
   (d) 3096 m   (e) 3040 m   (f) 4009 m

Exercise 4, pages 11-14

7. Find the value of 1 km − 350 m.

1000 m − 350 m = ☐

350 m + ☐ = 1000 m

1 km − 350 m = ☐ m

1 km = 1000 m

1000 = 900 + 90 + 10

	9 hundreds	10 tens
−	3 hundreds	5 tens
	6 hundreds	5 tens

8. Find the value of 1 km − 5 m.

1 km − 5 m = ☐ m

1000
900 90 10

10 − 5 = 5

9. Find the value of 1 km − 355 m.

1 km − 355 m = ☐ m

1000
900 90 10

900 − 300 = 600
90 − 50 = 40
10 −   5 =   5

10. Find the value of 2 km − 1 km 625 m.

2 km − 1 km 625 m = ☐ m

2 km − 1 km = 1 km

1 km − 625 m = ☐ m

11. Find the value of 1 km 24 m − 789 m.

$$\begin{array}{r} 1\,0\,2\,4 \\ -\ \ 7\,8\,9 \\ \hline \end{array}$$

1 km 24 m − 789 m = ◻ m

12. Find the sum of 1 km 456 m and 879 m.

$$\begin{array}{r} 1\,4\,5\,6 \\ +\ \ 8\,7\,9 \\ \hline \end{array}$$

1 km 456 m + 879 m = ◻ km ◻ m

Exercise 5, pages 15-16

13. Find the missing numbers.

(a) 1 km − 240 m = ◻ m   (b) 1 km − 248 m = ◻ m

(c) 1 km − 45 m = ◻ m   (d) 1 km − 7 m = ◻ m

(e) 324 m + ◻ m = 1 km   (f) 901 m + ◻ m = 1 km

(g) 2 km − 1 km 125 m = ◻ m

(h) 3 km − 2 m 45 m = ◻ m

(i) 1 km 485 m + 458 m = ◻ km ◻ m

(j) 4 km 903 m + 99 m = ◻ km ◻ m

17

14.

Bank   Post Office   Library

Find the distance between the bank and the library.

2 km 450 m + 1 km 850 m = ⬜ km ⬜ m

2 km 450 m $\xrightarrow{+1\,km}$ 3 km 450 m $\xrightarrow{+850\,m}$ 4 km 300 m

The distance between the bank and the library

is ⬜ km ⬜ m.

15.

School A   Train Station   School B

Which school is nearer to the train station?
How much nearer?

1 km 40 m − 920 m = ⬜ m

School B is ⬜ m nearer to the train station.

16. Add or subtract in compound units.

(a) 4 km 325 m + 5 km   (b) 3 km 650 m + 240 m
(c) 7 km 800 m + 300 m   (d) 2 km 180 m + 4 km 65 m
(e) 9 km 150 m − 3 km   (f) 5 km 950 m − 150 m
(g) 5 km − 400 m   (h) 6 km 150 m − 2 km 200 m
(i) 4 km 350 m − 800 m   (j) 8 km 5 m − 5 m 750 m

Exercise 6, pages 17-18

1. Write in centimeters.
   (a) 4 m
   (b) 1 m 40 cm
   (c) 2 m 25 cm

2. Write in meters and centimeters.
   (a) 120 cm
   (b) 225 cm
   (c) 309 cm

3. Find the missing numbers.

   (a) 1 m − 65 cm = ☐ cm

   (b) 2 m − 1 m 75 cm = ☐ cm

   (c) 3 m − 2 m 92 cm = ☐ cm

4. Add or subtract in compound units.
   (a) 2 m 75 cm + 3 m
   (b) 3 m 4 cm + 65 cm
   (c) 5 m 85 cm − 5 cm
   (d) 5 m 90 cm − 76 cm

5. Kwame is 1 m 60 cm tall.
   Ryan is 16 cm shorter than Kwame.
   What is Ryan's height?

6. Write in meters.
   (a) 3 km
   (b) 1 km 450 m
   (c) 2 km 506 m

7. Write in kilometers and meters.
   (a) 1680 m
   (b) 1085 m
   (c) 2204 m

8. Find the missing numbers.

   (a) 1 km − 800 m = ☐ m

   (b) 2 km − 1 km 45 m = ☐ m

   (c) 5 km − 4 km 940 m = ☐ m

9. Add or subtract in compound units.
   (a) 2 km 650 m + 3 km
   (b) 3 km 300 m + 800 m
   (c) 5 km 950 m − 4 km
   (d) 6 km 25 m − 3 km 350 m

3 Yards, Feet and Inches

Get a yard stick and find out how long 1 yard is.
Estimate the length of the teacher's desk in your classroom.
Check by measuring it.

Is the length of your teacher's desk more than 2 yards?

Get a ruler and find out how long 1 foot is.
Estimate the length of your math book.
Check by measuring with your ruler.

Is your math book less than a foot long?

Take a look at your ruler again.
Is your math book about 10 inches long?

1. A table is 1 yd 2 ft long.

   (a) 1 yd 2 ft is [ ] ft more than 1 yd.

   (b) 1 yd 2 ft = [ ] ft

The **yard (yd)**, **foot (ft)** and **inch (in.)** are units of length.

1 yd = 3 ft
1 ft = 12 in.

2. A ribbon is 11 yd 2 ft. Write the length in feet.

To change yards to feet, we multiply by 3.

$$1 \text{ yd} = 1 \times 3 = 3 \text{ ft}$$
$$2 \text{ yd} = 2 \times 3 = 6 \text{ ft}$$

3. (a) Write 8 yd in feet.

8 yd = ⬜ ft

To change feet to yards, we divide by 3.

(b) Write 18 ft in yards.

18 ft = ⬜ yd

$$3 \text{ ft} = 3 \div 3 = 1 \text{ yd}$$
$$6 \text{ ft} = 6 \div 3 = 2 \text{ yd}$$

4. The length of the sofa is 15 ft.

The sofa is ⬜ yd long.

20 ft
/ \
18 ft   2 ft

5. (a) 20 ft = ⬜ yd ⬜ ft

(b) 25 ft = ⬜ yd ⬜ ft

$$25 \div 3 = 8 \text{ R } 1$$
$$25 \text{ yd} = 8 \text{ yd } 1 \text{ ft}$$

(c) 422 ft = ⬜ yd ⬜ ft

$$3\overline{)422}$$

6. The coffee table is 1 ft 5 in. high.

(a) 1 ft 5 in. is ⬜ in. more than 1 ft.

(b) 1 ft 5 in. = ⬜ in.

To change feet to inches, we multiply by 12.

7. (a) Write 7 ft in inches.

$$1 \text{ ft} = 1 \times 12 = 12 \text{ in.}$$
$$2 \text{ ft} = 2 \times 12 = 24 \text{ in.}$$

7 ft = ⬜ in.

(b) Write 7 ft 3 in. in inches.

7 ft 3 in. = ⬜ in.

8. Measure the width of your classroom door in feet and inches. Then write the width in inches.

9. Find the missing numbers.

(a) 6 yd = ☐ ft

(b) 32 yd = ☐ ft

(c) 9 yd 2 ft = ☐ ft

(d) 12 yd 1 ft = ☐ ft

(e) 30 ft = ☐ yd ☐ ft

(f) 24 ft = ☐ yd ☐ ft

(g) 123 ft = ☐ yd ☐ ft

(h) 100 ft = ☐ yd ☐ ft

(i) 1 ft 5 in. = ☐ in.

(j) 4 ft = ☐ in.

(k) 4 ft 9 in. = ☐ in.

(l) 6 ft 4 in. = ☐ in.

Exercise 7, pages 19-20

10. Find the value of 2 ft + 2 ft in yards and feet.

2 ft + 2 ft = ☐ yd ☐ ft

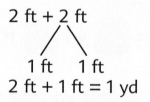

2 ft + 2 ft

1 ft   1 ft
2 ft + 1 ft = 1 yd

11. What is the sum of 3 yd 2 ft and 2 yd 2 ft?

3 yd 2 ft —+2 yd→ 5 yd 2 ft —+2 ft→ 6 yd 1 ft

3 yd 2 ft + 2 yd 2 ft = ☐ yd ☐ ft

12. (a) 1 yd − 2 ft = ☐ ft

(b) 12 yd − 2 ft = ☐ yd ☐ ft

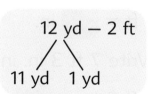

12 yd − 2 ft

11 yd   1 yd

13. How long are two paper strips, each
    11 inches long, taped together?

    11 in. + 11 in. = ☐ ft ☐ in.

    11 in. + 1 in. = 1 ft
    11 in. + 11 in.
    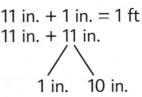
    1 in.   10 in.

14. Find the value of 1 ft − 8 in.

    1 ft − 8 in. = ☐ in.

    1 ft = 12 in.

    8 in. + ☐ = 1 ft

15. (a) 6 ft − 8 in. = ☐ ft ☐ in.

    6 ft − 8 in.
    5 ft   1 ft

    (b) 6 ft 4 in. − 8 in. = ☐ ft ☐ in.

16. A blue ribbon is 4 ft 7 in. long and a red ribbon
    is 1 ft 10 in. long.

    (a) Find the total length of the ribbons.

    4 ft 7 in.   **1 ft 10 in.**

    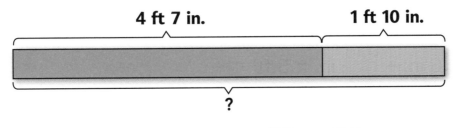

    ?

    4 ft 7 in. + 1 ft 10 in. = ☐ ft ☐ in.

    4 ft 7 in. $\xrightarrow{+1\text{ ft}}$ 5 ft 7 in. $\xrightarrow{+10\text{ in.}}$ 6 ft 5 in.

    The total length of the ribbons is ft in.

(b) How much longer is the blue ribbon than the red ribbon?

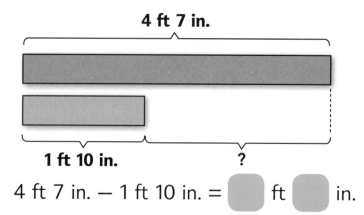

4 ft 7 in.

1 ft 10 in.   **?**

4 ft 7 in. − 1 ft 10 in. = ☐ ft ☐ in.

4 ft 7 in. $\xrightarrow{-1\,ft}$ 3 ft 7 in. $\xrightarrow{-10\,in.}$ 2 ft 9 in.

The blue ribbon is ☐ ft ☐ in. longer than the red ribbon.

17. Find the missing numbers.

(a) 7 in. + ☐ in. = 12 in.

(b) 3 in. + ☐ = 12 in.

(c) 4 ft. 6 in. + ☐ in. = 5 ft

(d) 4 ft. 6 in. + 8 in. = ☐ ft ☐ in.

(e) 1 ft 10 in. − 7 in. = ☐ in.

(f) 5 ft 10 in. − 3 ft 7 in. = ☐ ft ☐ in.

(g) 3 yd 2 ft + 6 yd 1 ft = ☐ yd

(h) 21 yd 1 ft − 10 yd 2 ft = ☐ yd ☐ ft

Exercise 8, pages 21-22

1. Write in feet.
   (a) 5 yd   (b) 87 yd 2 ft   (c) 308 yd 1 ft

2. Write in inches.
   (a) 9 ft   (b) 6 ft 10 in.   (c) 9 ft 9 in.

3. Write in yards and feet.
   (a) 27 ft   (b) 108 ft   (c) 212 ft

4. Write in feet and inches.
   (a) 12 in.   (b) 16 in.   (c) 24 in.

5. Find the missing numbers.
   (a) 1 yd − 2 ft = ☐ ft

   (b) 2 yd − 1 yd 1 ft = ☐ ft

   (c) 15 yd − 14 yd 2 ft = ☐ ft

   (d) 1 ft − 7 in. = ☐ in.

   (e) 13 ft − 12 ft 8 in. = ☐ in.

6. Add or subtract in compound units.
   (a) 5 yd 1 ft + 1 ft   (b) 8 yd 2 ft + 2 ft
   (c) 5 yd 1 ft + 2 yd 2 ft   (d) 3 yd 2 ft − 2 yd
   (e) 9 yd 1 ft − 2 ft   (f) 6 yd 1 ft − 5 yd 2 ft

7. Add or subtract in compound units.
   (a) 5 ft 11 in. + 7 ft   (b) 9 ft 5 in. + 6 in.
   (c) 8 ft 7 in. + 3 ft 8 in.   (d) 11 ft 11 in. − 6 in.
   (e) 10 ft 4 in. − 6 in.   (f) 6 ft 8 in. − 4 ft 10 in.

4 Miles

The **mile (mi)**, yard (yd), foot (ft) and inch (in.) are units of length.

1 mile = 5280 feet

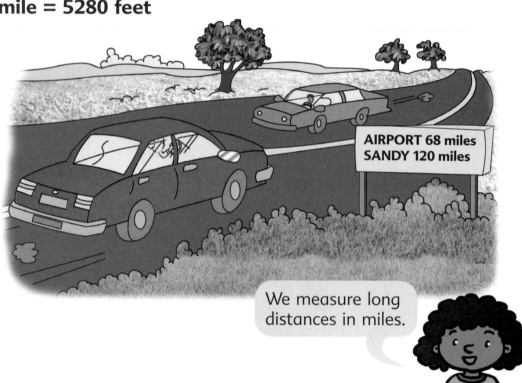

We measure long distances in miles.

1. Juan jogged 3 mi daily. How many miles did he jog in a week?

2.

San Francisco   Denver   New York

← 1260 mi →

← 2930 mi →

The distance between San Francisco and New York

is ⬚ mi.

Find the distance between New York and Denver.

26

Exercise 9, page 23

Find the value of each of the following:

	(a)	(b)	(c)
1.	65 + 28	34 + 66	18 + 84
2.	99 + 99	99 + 98	27 + 45
3.	78 − 45	90 − 56	90 − 85
4.	99 − 98	83 − 75	98 − 97
5.	4 × 30	50 × 8	200 × 9
6.	500 ÷ 5	600 ÷ 10	400 ÷ 2
7.	100 × 6	5 × 90	300 × 7
8.	160 ÷ 8	240 ÷ 3	810 ÷ 9
9.	6 × 100	40 × 6	500 × 5

10. (a) What number is 29 less than 84?
    (b) What number is 68 less than 310?
    (c) What number is 35 more than 475?
    (d) What number is 97 more than 5397?

11. There are 80 pages in one notebook.
    How many pages are there in 6 such notebooks?

12. A grocer packed 200 onions equally into 5 bags.
    How many onions were there in each bag?

13. Alex sold 70 muffins on Friday.
    He sold 4 times as many muffins on Sunday as on Friday.
    How many muffins did he sell on Sunday?

14. Find the missing numbers.

    (a) 23 × 2 × 10 = 230 × ☐   (b) 456 + ☐ = 465

    (c) 34 × 9 = 340 − ☐   (d) 350 − ☐ = 251

15. Find the value.
    Use estimation to see if your answers are reasonable.
    (a) 1062 × 6   (b) 458 × 8   (c) 99 × 9
    (d) 192 ÷ 7   (e) 8932 ÷ 5   (f) 847 ÷ 4

16. The cards below show the number of children who took part in three different activities.

Walkathon	Swimming competition	Carnival
56 boys	63 boys	45 boys
50 girls	66 girls	47 girls

    (a) Make a table to show the data.
    (b) Find the total number of children in the three activities.

17. Ivan rolled a number cube with the numbers 2, 3, 3, 4, 4, and 4.
    He rolled it 30 times.
    (a) Which number is he least likely to roll?
    (b) Which number is he likely to roll most often?

18. Fill in the missing numbers.
    (a) 3 m 95 cm = ☐ cm   (b) 4 m 5 cm = ☐ cm

    (c) 2 km 60 m = ☐ m   (d) 3 km 78 m = ☐ m

    (e) 4 yd = ☐ ft   (f) 12 yd 2 ft = ☐ ft

    (g) 6 ft = ☐ in.   (h) 3 ft 7 in. = ☐ in.

19. Find the missing numbers.

   (a) 618 cm = ☐ m ☐ cm   (b) 936 cm = ☐ m ☐ cm

   (c) 3090 m = ☐ km ☐ m   (d) 3999 m = ☐ km ☐ m

   (e) 33 ft = ☐ yd ☐ ft   (f) 1954 ft = ☐ yd ☐ ft

20. Add or subtract in compound units.

   (a) 1 m − 55 cm   (b) 2 m − 95 cm
   (c) 1 km − 600 m   (d) 12 km − 275 m
   (e) 1 m 26 cm + 2 m 65 cm   (f) 5 km 40 m − 3 km 990 m
   (g) 4 yd − 2 ft   (h) 10 ft 2 in. − 4 ft 8 in.

21. Mr. Cole tied two packages with these strings.

   1 m 80 cm   **1 m 65 cm**

   What was the total length of the strings?

22. Find the distance between the boat
    and the lighthouse.

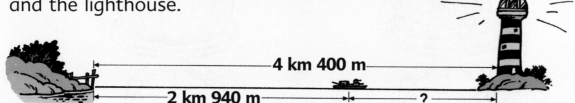

23. Mr. Marconi is 6 ft 2 in. tall.
    His son Josh is 3 ft 10 in. tall.
    How much shorter is Josh than his dad?

24. How many yards are there in a mile?

Review 6, pages 24-27

7 WEIGHT

1 Kilograms and Grams

The **kilogram (kg)** and **gram (g)** are units of weight.

1 kg = 1000 g

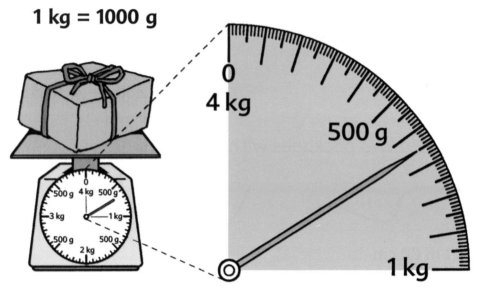

The package weighs 650 g.

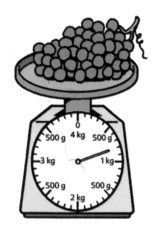

The grapes weigh

 g.

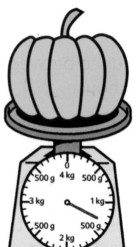

The pumpkin weighs

 kg g.

1. Read the scales.

(a)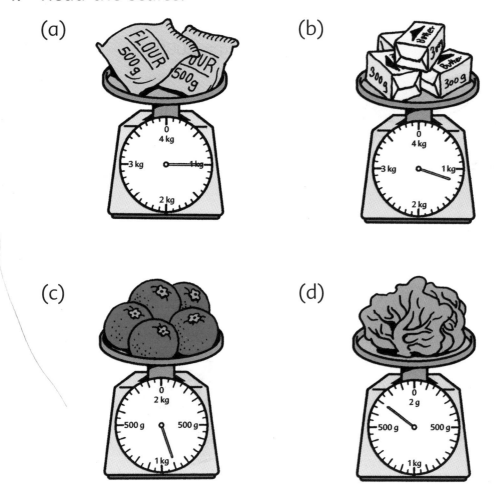

(b)

(c)

(d)

2. Estimate the weight of each of the following.
   Then check by weighing with a scale.

	My estimate	My measure
A 2 liter bottle of water	about [ ] kg	about [ ] kg [ ] g
A school bag	about [ ] kg	about [ ] kg [ ] g
A brick	about [ ] kg	about [ ] kg [ ] g

Exercise 1, pages 28-29

3. The potatoes weigh 2 kg 200 g.
   Write the weight in grams.

2 kg = 2000 g

4. Write in grams.
   (a) 1 kg 456 g   (b) 2 kg 370 g   (c) 3 kg 808 g
   (d) 2 kg 80 g   (e) 1 kg 8 g   (f) 4 kg 7 g

5. Each book weighs 350 g.
   The total weight of 4 books

   is ▢ kg ▢ g.

6. Write in kilograms and grams.
   (a) 2143 g   (b) 1354 g   (c) 3800 g
   (d) 2206 g   (e) 3085 g   (f) 4009 g

7.

1100 g

1 kg 250 g

Which is heavier, the fish or the chicken?
How much heavier?

Exercise 2, pages 30-33

8. A bag of peanuts weighs 1 kg 850 g.
   How much more peanuts are needed to make up 2 kg?

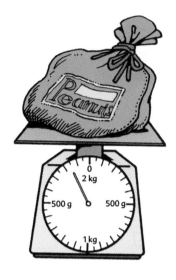

$$1 \text{ kg} - 850 \text{ g} = \boxed{} \text{ g}$$

$$2 \text{ kg} - 1 \text{ kg } 850 \text{ g} = \boxed{} \text{ g}$$

9. Find the missing numbers.

   (a) $1 \text{ kg} - 395 \text{ g} = \boxed{} \text{ g}$

   (b) $1 \text{ kg} - 85 \text{ g} = \boxed{} \text{ g}$

   (c) $3 \text{ kg} - 2 \text{ kg } 400 \text{ g} = \boxed{} \text{ g}$

   (d) $5 \text{ kg} - 4 \text{ kg } 60 \text{ g} = \boxed{} \text{ g}$

   (e) $1 \text{ kg} - 540 \text{ g} = \boxed{} \text{ g}$

   (f) $3 \text{ kg} - 805 \text{ g} = \boxed{} \text{ kg} \boxed{} \text{ g}$

10.

3 kg 80 g

1 kg 960 g

(a) Find the total weight of the watermelon and the bananas.

3 kg 80 g + 1 kg 960 g = kg g

3 kg 80 g $\xrightarrow{+1\,kg}$ 4 kg 80 g $\xrightarrow{+960\,g}$ 5 kg 40 g

The total weight is ⬜ kg ⬜ g.

(b) Find the difference in weight between the watermelon and the bananas.

3 kg 80 g − 1 kg 960 g = kg g

3 kg 80 g $\xrightarrow{-1\,kg}$ 2 kg 80 g $\xrightarrow{-960\,g}$ 1 kg 120 g

The difference in weight is ⬜ kg ⬜ g.

34

11.

Onions

2 kg 600 g

Tomatoes

1 kg 500 g

(a) What is the total weight of the onions and the tomatoes?

(b) What is the difference in weight between the onions and the tomatoes?

12. Add or subtract in compound units.
   (a) 3 kg 500 g + 2 kg
   (b) 4 kg 650 g + 450 g
   (c) 3 kg 100 g + 1 kg 900 g
   (d) 2 kg 50 g + 4 kg 70 g
   (e) 3 kg 10 g − 200 g
   (f) 4 kg 300 g − 1 kg 50 g
   (g) 4 kg 250 g − 1 kg 500 g
   (h) 5 kg − 2 kg 905 g

13. Lily weighed 25 kg 750 g two years ago.
    Now she weighs 32 kg.
    How much weight did she gain?

14. A pumpkin weighs 2 kg 990 g.
    A watermelon weighs 4 kg 200 g.
    (a) Find the total weight of the pumpkin and the watermelon.
    (b) Find the difference in weight between the pumpkin and the watermelon.

Exercise 3, pages 34-36

2 Word Problems

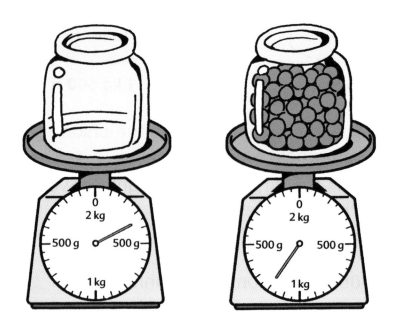

Weight of empty jar	+	Weight of marbles	=	Total weight of jar and marbles
(350 g)		(?)		(1 kg 200 g)

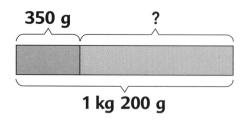

Weight of marbles = 1 kg 200 g − 350 g

$$= \boxed{} \text{ g}$$

1. A bottle of sauce weighs 560 g.
   The empty bottle weighs 305 g.
   How many grams of sauce are there in the bottle?

2. The total weight of a football and 10 tennis balls is 1 kg.
   If the weight of each tennis ball is 60 g, find the weight of the football.

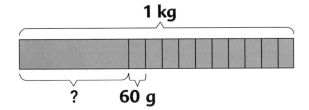

Weight of 10 tennis balls = 60 × 10
$\qquad\qquad\qquad\qquad\quad$ = 600 g

Weight of the football $\quad$ = 1 kg − 600 g

$\qquad\qquad\qquad\qquad\qquad$ = ⬜ g

The football weighs ⬜ g.

3. William's weight is 57 kg.
   He is 3 times as heavy as Sean.
   What is Sean's weight?

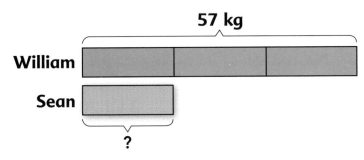

3 units = 57 kg

1 unit = ⬜ kg

Sean's weight is ⬜ kg.

4. A watermelon is 5 times as heavy as a grapefruit. If the grapefruit weighs 950 g, find the weight of the watermelon.

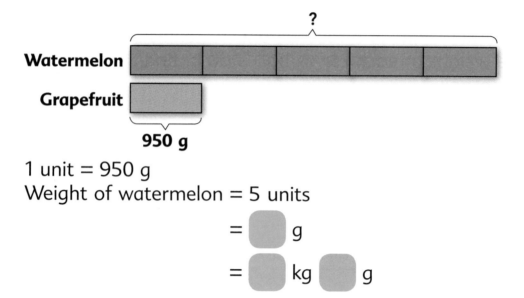

1 unit = 950 g
Weight of watermelon = 5 units

$$= \boxed{} \text{ g}$$

$$= \boxed{} \text{ kg } \boxed{} \text{ g}$$

5. John weighs 34 kg 600 g.
   He is 800 g heavier than David.
   What is David's weight?

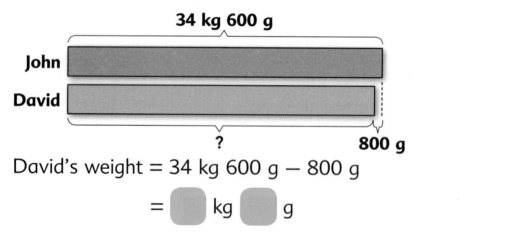

David's weight = 34 kg 600 g − 800 g

$$= \boxed{} \text{ kg } \boxed{} \text{ g}$$

6. A goose weighs 3 kg 200 g.
   A duck weighs 1 kg 800 g.
   (a) What is the total weight of the goose and the duck?
   (b) What is the difference in weight between the goose and the duck?

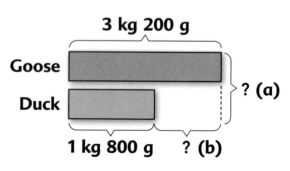

7. The total weight of a bottle of cooking oil and 2 bags of sugar is 5 kg 50 g.
   If the weight of each bag of sugar is 2 kg, find the weight of the bottle of cooking oil.

   Weight of 2 bags of sugar = ☐ kg

   Weight of the bottle of cooking oil = ☐ kg ☐ g

8. (a) Weight of the bag of rice = ☐ kg

   (b) The cost of the bag of rice is $5.

      Cost of 1 kg of rice = $☐

9. (a) Weight of the chicken = ☐ kg

   (b) Mrs. King paid $6 for the chicken.

      Cost of 1 kg of chicken = $☐

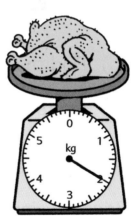

10. Mr. Handyman bought 8 kg of nails for $24.
    How much does 1 kg of nails cost?

Exercise 4, pages 37-39

1. Write in grams.
   - (a) 5 kg
   - (b) 1 kg 950 g
   - (c) 1 kg 60 g
   - (d) 2 kg 805 g
   - (e) 2 kg 5 g
   - (f) 3 kg 2 g

2. Write in kilograms and grams.
   - (a) 1905 g
   - (b) 1055 g
   - (c) 2208 g
   - (d) 3390 g
   - (e) 3599 g
   - (f) 5002 g

3. Add or subtract in compound units.
   - (a) 2 kg 940 g + 300 g
   - (b) 3 kg 880 g + 1 kg 220 g
   - (c) 4 kg − 1 kg 480 g
   - (d) 5 kg 20 g − 2 kg 450 g

4.

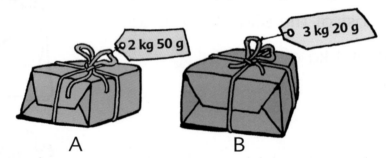

A   B

   - (a) Find the total weight of the two packages.
   - (b) Find the difference in weight between the two packages.

5. The total weight of Ali and Sam is 100 kg.
   If Ali's weight is 46 kg 540 g, find Sam's weight.

6. Brian's weight is 70 kg.
   He is 5 times as heavy as his son.
   Find the total weight of Brian and his son.

7. David weighs 39 kg.
   Hugh is twice as heavy as David.
   Matthew weighs 27 kg less than Hugh.
   What is Matthew's weight?

8. A 10-kg bag of apples cost $5.
   How much does 1 kg of apples cost?

③ Pounds and Ounces

The **pound (lb)** and **ounce (oz)** are units of weight.

1 lb = 16 oz

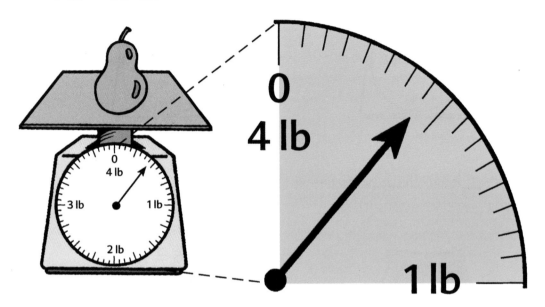

The pear weighs 7 oz.

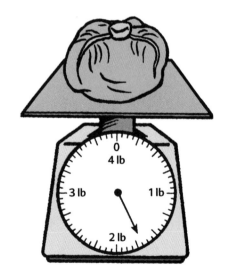

The mushrooms weigh

☐ oz.

The cabbage weighs

☐ lb ☐ oz.

1. Read the scales.
   (a)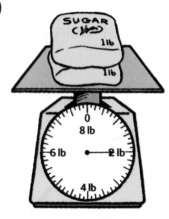

   (b)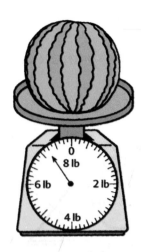

2. The sack of flour weighs 4 lb 13 oz.
   Write the weight in oz.

   $1\ lb = 1 \times 16 = 16\ oz$
   $4\ lb = 4 \times 16 = 64\ oz$

3. Write in ounces.
   (a) 5 lb   (b) 7 lb 15 oz   (c) 9 lb 9 oz

4. Each stick of butter weighs 8 oz.
   The total weight of 3 sticks of

   butter is ▢ lb ▢ oz.

   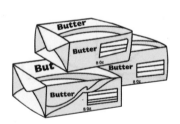

5. Write in pounds and ounces.
   (a) 16 oz   (b) 20 oz   (c) 26 oz

6. Find the difference between 1 lb and 14 oz.

1 lb − 14 oz = ☐ oz   1 lb = 16 oz
                        16 oz − 14 oz = 2 oz

7. Find the difference between 3 lb and 10 oz.

1 lb − 10 oz = ☐ oz

3 lb − 10 oz = 2 lb ☐ oz

3 lb

2 lb   1 lb

8. Find the sum of 12 oz and 9 oz.

12 oz + ☐ = 1 lb

12 oz + 9 oz = 1 lb ☐ oz

12 oz + 9 oz

4 oz   5 oz

9. Find the missing numbers.

(a) 1 lb − 9 oz = ☐ oz

(b) 5 lb − 4 oz = 4 lb ☐ oz

(c) 14 oz + 10 oz = 1 lb ☐ oz

(d) 3 lb 11 oz + 3 lb 6 oz = 7 lb ☐ oz

(e) 10 lb − 3 oz = ☐ lb ☐ oz

(f) 2 lb 15 oz + 15 oz = ☐ lb ☐ oz

Exercise 5, pages 40-41

10.

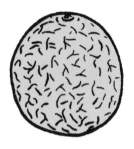

1 lb 14 oz   **3 lb 9 oz**

(a) Find the total weight of the cantaloupe and the grapes.

3 lb 9 oz + 1 lb 14 oz = ▢ lb ▢ oz

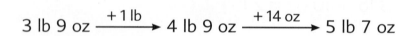

3 lb 9 oz $\xrightarrow{+\,1\,\text{lb}}$ 4 lb 9 oz $\xrightarrow{+\,14\,\text{oz}}$ 5 lb 7 oz

The total weight is ▢ lb ▢ oz.

(b) Find the difference in weight between the cantaloupe and the grapes.

3 lb 9 oz − 1 lb 14 oz = ▢ lb ▢ oz.

3 lb 9 oz $\xrightarrow{-\,1\,\text{lb}}$ 2 lb 9 oz $\xrightarrow{-\,14\,\text{oz}}$ 1 lb 11 oz

The difference in weight is ▢ lb ▢ oz.

11.

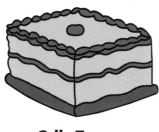

3 lb 7 oz   **2 lb 10 oz**

    (a) Find the total weight of the two cakes.
    (b) What is the difference in weight between the first
           cake and the second cake?

12. The total weight of two watermelons is 21 lb.
    The bigger watermelon weighs 12 lb 9 oz.
    What is the weight of the smaller watermelon?

13. A tomato weighs 3 oz.
    An avocado weighs 4 oz more than the tomato.
    A squash is twice as heavy as the avocado.
    What is the weight of the squash?

14. A pumpkin weighs 21 lb.
    The pumpkin is 7 times as heavy as a bunch of bananas.
    What is the total weight of the pumpkin and the bunch
    of bananas?

Exercise 6, pages 42-43

REVIEW 7

Find the value of each of the following:

	(a)	(b)	(c)
1.	499 + 42	507 + 3593	3084 + 63
2.	750 − 145	1806 − 82	7009 − 5
3.	53 × 7	156 × 5	407 × 4
4.	87 ÷ 3	104 ÷ 8	324 ÷ 6

5. There are 24 boxes of cherries in a carton.
   How many boxes of cherries are there in 8 cartons?

6. 5 people shared $450 equally.
   How much money did each person receive?

7. Lindsey gave each of her friends 7 cupcakes.
   She gave away 140 cupcakes altogether.
   How many friends did she give the cupcakes to?

8. There are 8 boxes of yellow and green buttons.
   There are 46 buttons in each box.
   If there are 200 yellow buttons, how many
   green buttons are there?

9. There were 150 bulbs in a box.
   6 of them were broken.
   The rest were packed into boxes of 4 bulbs each.
   How many boxes of bulbs were there?

10. Mr. Wang bought 3 boxes of oranges.
    There were 36 oranges in the first box.
    There were 54 oranges in each of the other two boxes.
    How many oranges did he buy?

Find the missing numbers.

11. (a) 5 m = ⬜ cm   (b) 4 m 8 cm = ⬜ cm

    (c) 2 km 560 m = ⬜ m   (d) 3 km 5 m = ⬜ m

    (e) 1 kg 30 g = ⬜ g   (f) 2 kg 80 g = ⬜ g

    (g) 3 lb 2 oz = ⬜ oz   (h) 18 oz = ⬜ lb ⬜ oz

12. (a) 208 cm = ⬜ m ⬜ cm

    (b) 1850 m = ⬜ km ⬜ m

    (c) 3095 g = ⬜ kg ⬜ g

Add or subtract in compound units.

13. (a) 1 m 58 cm + 70 cm   (b) 2 m 95 cm + 2 m 45 cm
    (c) 3 m − 2 m 35 cm   (d) 4 m 5 cm − 1 m 85 cm
    (e) 5 km 690 m + 520 m   (f) 7 km 960 m + 2 km 240 m
    (g) 9 km 420 m − 780 m   (h) 8 km 30 m − 3 km 480 m
    (i) 4 kg 920 g + 125 g   (j) 3 kg 760 g + 4 kg 350 g
    (k) 6 kg − 4 kg 820 g   (l) 4 kg 25 g − 2 kg 230 g
    (m) 7 lb 5 oz + 14 oz   (n) 5 lb 11 oz + 3 lb 11 oz
    (o) 12 lb − 8 lb 2 oz   (p) 3 lb 1 oz − 1 lb 15 oz

14. (a) The total weight of the fruits is ⬜ g.

    (b) If the apple weighs 90 g, find the
        total weight of the two pears.

    (c) If the pears are of the same weight,
        find the weight of each pear.

47

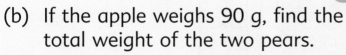

8 CAPACITY

1 Liters and Milliliters

How much water is there in each of these beakers?

The beakers are marked in **liters (ℓ)** and **milliliters (ml)**.

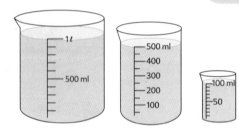

What is the total amount of water in each set of beakers?

(a)

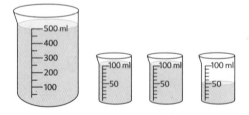

(b)

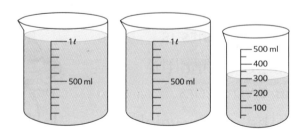

48

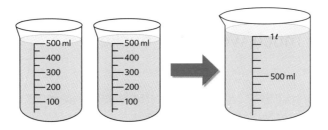

1 ℓ = 1000 ml

1.

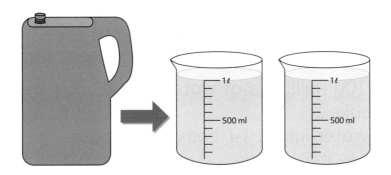

The bottle holds 2 liters of water.

Its **capacity** is ⬜ liters.

The capacity of a container is the amount it can hold.

We measure capacity in liters and milliliters.

2. Get some paper cups.
Find out how many paper cups you can fill with 1 liter of water.

3. Get a bucket.
   Find out how much water the bucket
   can hold.

4. (a) Measure 100 milliliters of water with a
       100-ml beaker.
       Pour the water into a 1-ℓ beaker and note
       where the water level is.

   (b) Repeat (a) until the 1-ℓ beaker contains 1 liter of water.

   (c) 1 ℓ = ☐ ml

5. Get a teaspoon.
   Find out how many teaspoons of water will make up 10 ml.
   Then find the capacity of the teaspoon.

   The capacity of the teaspoon is about ☐ ml.

6. Get a paper cup.
   Estimate how many milliliters of water
   the paper cup can hold.
   Then check by measuring the capacity
   of the paper cup.

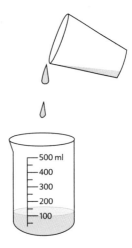

The capacity of the paper cup is about ⬜ ml.

7. Get any three small containers.
   Each container has a capacity of less than 1 liter.
   Label them A, B and C as shown.

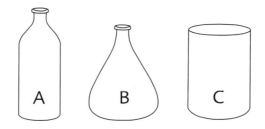

Estimate and then measure the capacity of each container.

Container	My estimate	My measure
A	about ⬜ ml	about ⬜ ml
B	about ⬜ ml	about ⬜ ml
C	about ⬜ ml	about ⬜ ml

8. Get a bucket, a basin and a big bottle.
   Each container has a capacity of more than 1 liter.
   Estimate how many liters of water will fill each container.
   Then check by measuring the capacities of the containers.

Container	My estimate	My measure		
a bucket	about ⬜ ℓ	about ⬜ ℓ	⬜ ml	
a basin	about ⬜ ℓ	about ⬜ ℓ	⬜ ml	
a big bottle	about ⬜ ℓ	about ⬜ ℓ	⬜ ml	

9. (a)

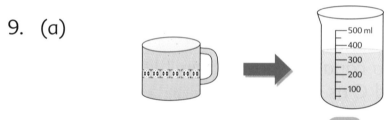

The capacity of the mug is ⬜ ml.

(b)

The capacity of the bottle is ⬜ ml.

(c)

The capacity of the jug is ⬜ ℓ ⬜ ml.

Exercise 1, pages 49-50

10. Find the total amount of water in these two beakers.

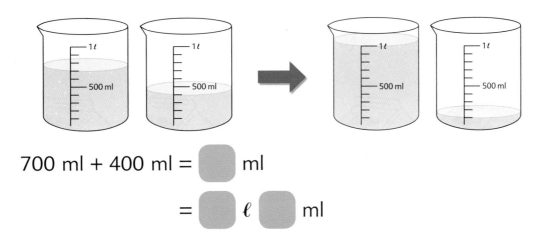

700 ml + 400 ml = ⬜ ml

= ⬜ ℓ ⬜ ml

11. Write 1500 ml in liters and milliliters.

1500 ml = ⬜ ℓ ⬜ ml

12. Write in liters and milliliters.
   (a) 1200 ml   (b) 2500 ml   (c) 2050 ml
   (d) 1005 ml   (e) 3400 ml   (f) 3105 ml

13. (a) Write 2 ℓ in milliliters.

      2 ℓ = ⬜ ml

   (b) Write 2 ℓ 350 ml in milliliters.

      2 ℓ 350 ml = ⬜ ml

14. Write in milliliters.

   (a) 1 ℓ 800 ml   (b) 1 ℓ 80 ml   (c) 1 ℓ 8 ml
   (d) 3 ℓ 25 ml   (e) 2 ℓ 5 ml   (f) 3 ℓ 500 ml

15.

   Each carton contains 250 ml of milk.
   The total amount of milk in 5 cartons is  ℓ   ml.

16.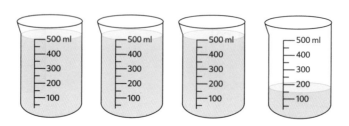

   How many milliliters more water are needed to make up
   2 liters?

17.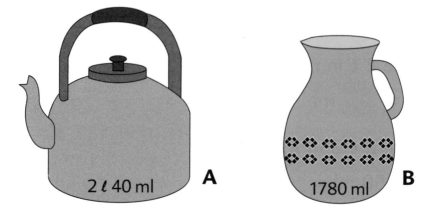

   Which container has the greater capacity?
   How much greater?

 Exercise 2, pages 51-53

18.

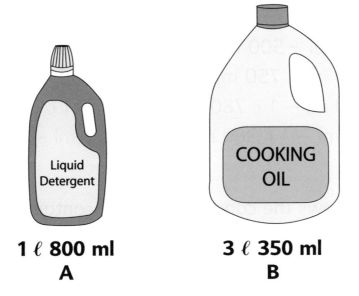

1 ℓ 800 ml
A

3 ℓ 350 ml
B

(a) Find the total capacity of the two containers.

1 ℓ 800 ml $\xrightarrow{+3\,\ell}$ 4 ℓ 800 ml $\xrightarrow{+350\text{ ml}}$ 5 ℓ 150 ml

1 ℓ 800 ml + 3 ℓ 350 ml = ▢ ℓ ▢ ml

The total capacity is ▢ ℓ ▢ ml.

(b) Find the difference in capacity between the two containers.

3 ℓ 350 ml $\xrightarrow{-1\,\ell}$ 2 ℓ 350 ml $\xrightarrow{-800\text{ ml}}$ 1 ℓ 550 ml

3 ℓ 350 ml − 1 ℓ 800 ml = ▢ ℓ ▢ ml

The difference in capacity is ▢ ℓ ▢ ml.

19. Add or subtract.

(a) 1 ℓ 500 ml + 500 ml

(b) 2 ℓ 800 ml + 1 ℓ 200 ml

(c) 3 ℓ 300 ml + 750 ml

(d) 5 ℓ 900 ml + 3 ℓ 240 ml

(e) 2 ℓ 800 ml − 1 ℓ 780 ml

(f) 4 ℓ − 1 ℓ 850 ml

(g) 4 ℓ 80 ml − 1 ℓ 360 ml

(h) 6 ℓ 5 ml − 2 ℓ 80 ml

20. The table shows the capacities of four containers.

Container A	2 ℓ 375 ml
Container B	1 ℓ 750 ml
Container C	1755 ml
Container D	2150 ml

(a) Which container has the greatest capacity?

(b) Which container has the smallest capacity?

(c) What is the total capacity of the four containers?

Exercise 3, pages 54-58

PRACTICE A

1. Write in milliliters.
   (a) 3 ℓ
   (b) 1 ℓ 200 ml
   (c) 2 ℓ 55 ml
   (d) 2 ℓ 650 ml
   (e) 3 ℓ 65 ml
   (f) 4 ℓ 5 ml

2. Write in liters and milliliters.
   (a) 5000 ml
   (b) 1600 ml
   (c) 2250 ml
   (d) 3205 ml
   (e) 2074 ml
   (f) 1009 ml

3. Write >, < or = in place of each .

   (a) 1 ℓ ⬤ 980 ml

   (b) 2 ℓ 50 ml ⬤ 2050 ml

   (c) 4 ℓ 8 ml ⬤ 4800 ml

4. The capacity of Container A is 2 ℓ 650 ml.
   The capacity of Container B is 5 ℓ 300 ml.
   (a) What is the total capacity of the two containers?
   (b) How much more water can Container B hold than Container A?

5. Container X holds 2 ℓ 800 ml of water.
   Container Y holds 1 ℓ 600 ml more water than Container X.
   How much water does Container Y hold?

6. Mrs. Chavez fills a container with 9 cartons of orange juice.
   Each carton contains 2 liters of orange juice.
   What is the capacity of the container?

② Gallons, Quarts, Pints and Cups

How much water is there in each of these containers?

Remember?
1 gallon   = 4 quarts or
                 2 half-gallons
1 half-gallon = 2 quarts
1 quart   = 2 pints
1 pint   = 2 cups

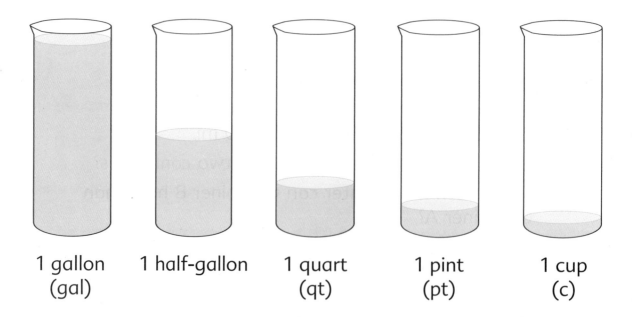

1 gallon   1 half-gallon   1 quart   1 pint   1 cup
(gal)   (qt)   (pt)   (c)

1. Look at some measuring cups.
   Can you find the markings for quarts, pints and cups?

2.

This jug holds 1 quart of water.
Its capacity is 1 quart.

1 quart of water = 2 pints of water
We can also say the capacity of this jug is 2 pints.

Do you know the capacity of this jug in cups?

3. Find the total amount of water in these two containers.

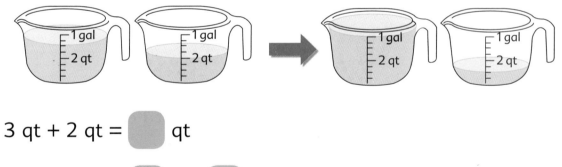

3 qt + 2 qt = ☐ qt

= ☐ gal ☐ qt

4. Write 78 qt in gallons and quarts.

78 qt = ☐ gal ☐ qt

5. Write 15 pt in quarts and pints.

$$1 \text{ qt} = 2 \text{ pt}$$

6. Write 21 c in pints and cups.

7.

Each carton contains 1 pt of milk.
The total amount of milk in the five cartons is qt pt.

Exercise 4, pages 59-60

8.

2 pt 1 c

3 pt 1 c

(a) Find the total capacity of the two jugs.

2 pt 1 c $\xrightarrow{+3 \text{ pt}}$ 5 pt 1 c $\xrightarrow{+1 \text{ c}}$ ☐ pt

The total capacity is ☐ pt.

The total capacity is also ☐ qt.

60

(b) Find the difference between the capacities of the two jugs.

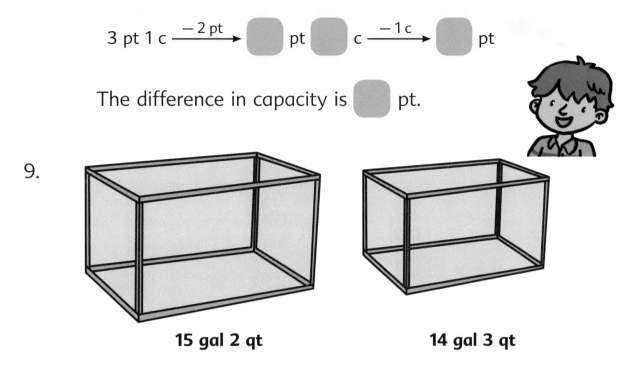

3 pt 1 c ──−2 pt──▶ ☐ pt ☐ c ──−1 c──▶ ☐ pt

The difference in capacity is ☐ pt.

9.

15 gal 2 qt   **14 gal 3 qt**

(a) What is the total capacity of the two fish tanks?

15 gal 2 qt + 14 gal 3 qt = ☐ gal ☐ qt

(b) What is the difference in the capacity of the two fish tanks?

15 gal 2 qt − 14 gal 3 qt = ☐ gal ☐ qt

10. Add or subtract in compound units.
   (a) 12 pt 1 c + 6 pt 1 c
   (b) 12 gal 3 qt + 9 gal 3 qt
   (c) 10 gal 1 qt − 8 gal 3 qt
   (d) 36 qt − 15 qt 3 c

Exercise 5, page 61

PRACTICE B

1. Write in cups.
    (a) 8 pt   (b) 15 pt 1 c

2. Write in pints.
    (a) 7 qt   (b) 11 qt 1 pt

3. Write in quarts.
    (a) 10 gal   (b) 23 gal 1 qt

4. Write >, < or = in place of each 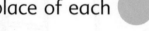.

    (a) 5 gal 1 qt ◯ 12 qt

    (b) 12 qt 1 pt ◯ 23 pt

    (c) 15 c ◯ 7 pt 1 c

5. Add or subtract.

    (a) 3 qt 1 pt + 7 qt 1 pt = ▢

    (b) 12 gal − 7 gal 1 qt = ▢

    (c) 258 pt − 185 pt 1 c = ▢

6. Container A holds 13 gal of water.
    Container B holds 7 gal 1 qt less water than Container A.
    How much water does Container B hold?

7. The capacity of a kettle is 2 qt.
    There is 1 pt of water in the kettle now.
    How many more pints of water are needed to fill
    up the kettle?

8. Morgan drinks 2 c of milk daily.
    How many pints of milk does she drink in a week?

REVIEW 8

Find the value of each of the following:

	(a)	(b)	(c)
1.	50 × 3	60 × 5	30 × 6
2.	40 ÷ 2	80 ÷ 4	600 ÷ 3
3.	6 × 90	7 × 400	300 × 8
4.	270 ÷ 9	320 ÷ 8	720 ÷ 9

5. Alice saves $50 a month.
   How much does she save in 8 months?

6. A cake shop sold 200 muffins.
   It sold 4 times as many muffins as chocolate cakes.
   How many chocolate cakes did it sell?

7. A fruit seller bought 9 boxes of pears.
   There were 40 pears in each box.
   How many pears did he buy altogether?

8. There are 6 coins in a set.
   How many coins are there in 200 sets?

9. Chris packed 250 tomatoes into bags of 5 each.
   (a) How many bags of tomatoes were there?
   (b) He sold all the tomatoes at $2 a bag.
       How much money did he receive?

10. (a) Brian bought 98 blue pens and 62 red pens.
        How many pens did he buy altogether?
    (b) He divided the pens equally into 8 boxes.
        How many pens were there in each box?

11. Find the missing numbers.

(a) 9 m 9 cm = ⬜ cm

(b) 405 cm = ⬜ m ⬜ cm

(c) 4 km 9 m = ⬜ m

(d) 4001 m = ⬜ km ⬜ m

12. Justin's school is 1 mile away from his home.

His school is ⬜ feet away from his home.

13. Write in inches.

(a) 9 ft 6 in.   (b) 5 ft 10 in.   (c) 7 ft 7 in.

14. Add or subtract in compound units.

(a) 5 lb 11 oz + 14 oz

(b) 8 ft 8 in. + 5 ft 5 in.

(c) 7 qt 1 pt + 11 qt 1 pt

(d) 12 lb 2 oz − 6 lb 12 oz

(e) 5 ft 1 in. − 2 ft 3 in.

(f) 17 gal − 10 gal 1 qt

15. The capacity of a container is 24 liters.
How many buckets of water are needed to fill up the
container if the capacity of the bucket is 3 liters?

16. The capacity of a container is 8 liters.
It contains 4 ℓ 650 ml of water.
How much more water is needed to fill up the container?

17. Adam bought 6 cans of paint.
    Each can contained 3 liters of paint.
    He had 2 ℓ 400 ml of paint left after painting his house.
    How much paint did he use?

18. A box of cherries weighs 1 lb 5 oz.
    A box of peaches weighs 14 oz more than the cherries.
    How much does the box of peaches weigh?
    What is the total weight of the box of cherries and the box
    of peaches?

19. The total weight of 2 bags of sugar and 1 bag of flour is
    4 lb 2 oz.
    If the weight of each bag of sugar is 10 oz, find the weight
    of the bag of flour.

9 MONEY

① Dollars and Cents

Read the prices of these items.

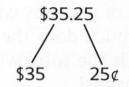

$35.25

$35   25¢

The dot . separates the cents from the dollars.

$35.25

$35.25 = ☐ dollars ☐ cents

$67.25

$67.25 = ☐ dollars ☐ cents

$75.40

$75.40 = ☐ dollars ☐ cents

$32.75

$32.75 = ☐ dollars ☐ cents

1. How much money is there in each set?

(a)

⬜ dollars ⬜ cents = $ ⬜

(b)

⬜ dollars ⬜ cents = $ ⬜

2. (a) Write $1.25 in cents.

$1.25 = ⬜ ¢

$1 = 100¢

(b) Write 170¢ in dollars and cents.

170¢ = $ ⬜

3. Write in cents.

(a) $0.30   (b) $1.95   (c) $4.05

4. Write in dollars and cents.

(a) 85¢   (b) 160¢   (c) 345¢

5. How much more money is needed to make $1?

(a) $0.70 + $ ⬜ = $1   (b) $0.55 + $ ⬜ = $1

 Exercise 1, pages 67-68

1. Write in cents.
   (a) $0.20   (b) $0.65   (c) $7.00
   (d) $2.05   (e) $5.60   (f) $3.95

2. Write in dollars and cents.
   (a) 5¢   (b) 60¢   (c) 400¢
   (d) 210¢   (e) 855¢   (f) 305¢

3. Find the missing amount of money in each of the following:
   (a) 30¢ + ⬜ = $1   (b) ⬜ + 45¢ = $1
   (c) $0.40 + ⬜ = $1   (d) ⬜ + $0.65 = $1

4. (a)

   6 quarters = $⬜

   (b)

   12 nickels = $⬜

   (c) Lily has 6 quarters and 12 nickels.
       How much money does she have altogether?

5. There are 4 nickels, 2 quarters and 4 one-dollar bills
   in a purse.
   What is the total amount of money in the purse?

② Addition

Morgan bought a box of plums for $13.25 and a cake for $6.50.
How much did she spend altogether?

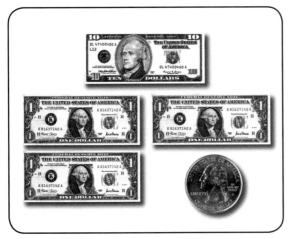

Cost of plums

Cost of cake

Total cost of plums and cake

$13.25 + $6.50 = $ [ ]

She spent $ [ ] altogether.

1. Find the value of
   (a) $1.50 + 20¢   (b) $14.20 + 65¢   (c) $38.40 + 35¢
   (d) $2.75 + 25¢   (e) $25.40 + 60¢   (f) $33.85 + 15¢

2. (a) $2.85 + 20¢ = $ ⬜

   (b) $2.70 + 60¢ = $ ⬜

   (c) $5.65 + 45¢ = $ ⬜

   (d) $16.95 + 45¢ = $ ⬜

   (e) $24.70 + 95¢ = $ ⬜

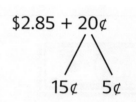

$2.85 + 20¢

15¢   5¢

85¢ and 15¢ make $1.

3. (a) $25.70 —+ $4→ $ ⬜ —+ 10¢→ $ ⬜

   $25.70 + $4.10 = $ ⬜

   (b) $34.65 —+ $2→ $ ⬜ —+ 35¢→ $ ⬜

   $34.65 + $2.35 = $ ⬜

   (c) $30.80 —+ $5→ $ ⬜ —+ 40¢→ $ ⬜

   $30.80 + $5.40 = $ ⬜

   (d) $24.70 —+ $10→ $ ⬜ —+ 50¢→ $ ⬜

   $24.70 + $10.50 = $ ⬜

4. Find the value of
   (a) $14.65 + $6.20   (b) $13.60 + $24.40
   (c) $32.70 + $24.50   (d) $15.60 + $23.70
   (e) $40.85 + $19.65   (f) $28.35 + $26.75

5. We can add $24.55 and $13.65 like this:

```
  $24.55
+ $13.65
─────────
  $38.20
```

```
    1 1
  2455
+ 1365
──────
  3820
```

Use this method to find the value of

(a) $35.30 + $21.40
(b) $27.10 + $10.90
(c) $40.70 + $33.60
(d) $52.85 + $16.35
(e) $28.65 + $32.45
(f) $36.90 + $24.85

Exercise 2, pages 69-71

6. Ali bought a toy car for $6.95.
   He also spent $2.80 on a meal.
   How much money did he spend altogether?

$2.80 + $6.95 = $ ⬜

He spent $ ⬜ altogether.

7. Miguel paid $11.90 for a pen.
   He had $24.65 left.
   How much money did he have at first?

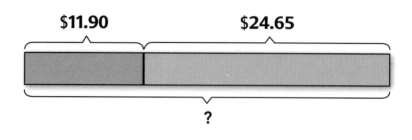

$11.90 + $24.65 = $ ⬜

He had $ ⬜ at first.

8. John saves $6.75 this week.
   He saves $2.35 less this week than last week.
   How much money did he save last week?

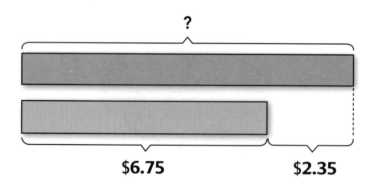

$6.75 + $2.35 = $ ⬜

He saved $ ⬜ last week.

Exercise 3, pages 72-73

③ Subtraction

Chris bought a radio and a calculator for $56.50.
The calculator cost $25.30.
How much did the radio cost?

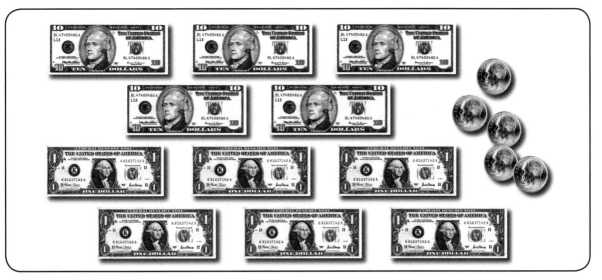

Cost of radio and calculator

Cost of calculator

Cost of radio

$56.50 − $25.30 = $ ⬜

The radio cost $ ⬜.

1. Find the value of
   (a) $2.60 − 20¢   (b) $8.75 − 30¢   (c) $35.85 − 45¢
   (d) $1.50 − 25¢   (e) $6.50 − 45¢   (f) $46.70 − 25¢

2. (a) $1 − 60¢ = ☐ ¢   (b) $1.30 − 60¢ = ☐ ¢

   (c) $1.25 − 35¢ = ☐ ¢   (d) $1.40 − 85¢ = ☐ ¢

3. (a) $3.20 − 80¢ = $☐

   (b) $14.65 − 90¢ = $☐

   (c) $46.25 − 45¢ = $☐

   (d) $32.05 − 85¢ = $☐

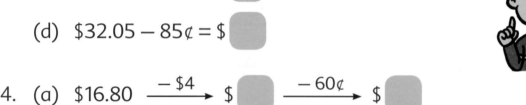

$3.20 − 80¢

$2.20 $1

Subtract 80¢ from $1.

4. (a) $16.80 ──− $4──→ $☐ ──− 60¢──→ $☐

      $16.80 − $4.60 = $☐

   (b) $37.70 ──− $10──→ $☐ ──− 20¢──→ $☐

      $37.70 − $10.20 = $☐

   (c) $29.20 ──− $12──→ $☐ ──− 50¢──→ $☐

      $29.20 − $12.50 = $☐

5. Find the value of
   (a) $47.50 − $12   (b) $35.70 − $0.85
   (c) $58 − $12.60   (d) $64.40 − $11.60
   (e) $25.05 − $15.35   (f) $56.20 − $28.95

6. We can subtract $23.70 from $46.20 like this:

$$\begin{array}{r} \$4\,6.2\,0 \\ -\ \$2\,3.7\,0 \\ \hline \$2\,2.5\,0 \end{array}$$

$$\begin{array}{r} {}^{5\ 12}4\,6\,2\,0 \\ -\ \ \ 2\,3\,7\,0 \\ \hline 2\,2\,5\,0 \end{array}$$

Use this method to find the value of
(a) $45.10 − $23.40
(b) $36.35 − $10.85
(c) $94.60 − $37.80
(d) $52.25 − $35.45
(e) $70.20 − $28.75
(f) $65.05 − $35.15

7. Find the value of
(a) 6200 − 415
(b) $62.00 − $4.15
(c) 4005 − 835
(d) $40.05 − $8.35

8. Find the value of
(a) $10 − $4.70
(b) $30 − $7.20
(c) $50 − $8.25
(d) $50 − $23.80
(e) $100 − $52.90
(f) $100 − $39.45

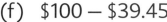

Exercise 4, pages 74-76

9. Nancy bought a tin of cookies which cost $5.65.
She gave the cashier $10.
How much change did she receive?

$$\$10 − \$5.65 = \$\boxed{}$$

She received $ change.

10. Mei had $20.
    She bought an umbrella and had $14.60 left.
    What was the cost of the umbrella?

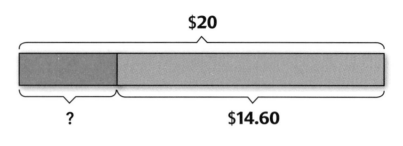

$20 − $14.60 = $ ⬚

The umbrella cost $ ⬚.

11. Jim has $25.50.
    He wants to buy a watch which costs $35.
    How much more money does he need?

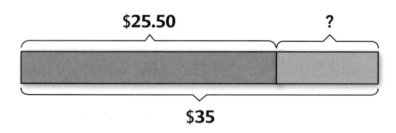

$35 − $25.50 = $ ⬚

He needs $ ⬚ more.

Exercise 5, pages 77-80

1. Add.
   (a) $26.20 + $13.50
   (b) $39.45 + $60.55
   (c) $48.40 + $27.30
   (d) $15.95 + $24.35
   (e) $65.85 + $25.80
   (f) $36.45 + $54.55

2. Subtract.
   (a) $36.70 − $15.35
   (b) $60.50 − $24.45
   (c) $52.30 − $30.70
   (d) $40.05 − $16.30
   (e) $72.20 − $26.95
   (f) $81.00 − $31.85

3. After spending $24.60, Holly had $76.40 left.
   How much money did she have at first?

4. Jerome wants to buy a fishing rod which costs $62.50.
   He has only $48.60.
   How much more money does he need?

5. A toy car costs $16.80.
   A toy airplane costs $5.60 more than the toy car.
   What is the cost of the toy airplane?

6. Sean had $10.
   After paying for his lunch, he had $6.95 left.
   How much did his lunch cost?

7. A shirt and a skirt cost $42.50.
   The shirt costs $16.85.
   What is the cost of the skirt?

8. Anne had $40.50.
   She bought a pen for $6.80 and a book for $13.20.
   How much money did she have left?

4 Multiplication and Division

Shane gets an allowance of $4.50 a week.
How much does he get in 6 weeks?

$4.50 = 450¢

$$
\begin{array}{r} \$4.50 \\ \times \quad 6 \\ \hline \$\boxed{} \end{array}
\qquad\longrightarrow\qquad
\begin{array}{r} 450 \\ \times \quad 6 \\ \hline 2700 \end{array}
$$

2700¢ = $\boxed{}$

He gets $\boxed{}$ in 6 weeks.

Carrie saved all her allowance for 9 weeks.
She has $49.50.
How much does she save each week?

$49.50 = 4950¢

$$
\boxed{} \\
9\,)\overline{\$49.50}
\qquad\longrightarrow\qquad
\begin{array}{r}
550 \\
9\,)\overline{4950} \\
45 \\
\hline
45 \\
45 \\
\end{array}
$$

550¢ = $\boxed{}$

She saves $\boxed{}$ a week.

78

1. Find the value of
   (a) 400¢ × 7
   (b) $4.00 × 7
   (c) 200¢ × 3
   (d) $20.00 × 3
   (e) 50¢ × 4
   (f) $0.50 × 4
   (g) 70¢ × 7
   (h) $0.70 × 7

2. There are 4 quarters in a dollar.

   $0.25 × 4 = $1.00

   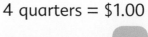

   4 quarters = $1.00

   8 quarters = $☐

   (a) What is the value of $0.25 × 8?
   (b) What is the value of $0.25 × 6?

3. There are 10 dimes in a dollar.

   $0.10 × 10 = $1.00

   (a) What is the value of $0.10 × 10?
   (b) What is the value of $0.10 × 20?

4. Estimate, then find the value of $8.75 × 5.

   $9 × 5 = $45

   The value of $8.75 × 5 is about $☐.

```
    $8.75
  ×     5
  _____
  ☐
```

```
      3 2
      8 7 5
  ×       5
  _____
    4 3 7 5
```

   The value of $8.75 × 5 is $☐.

5. Find the value of
   (a) $3.86 × 4
   (b) $8.93 × 5
   (c) $1.58 × 7
   (d) $7.04 × 8
   (e) $10.31 × 6
   (f) $43.20 × 2

6. A concert ticket costs $8.95.
   How much will 6 tickets cost?

   1 unit = $ ⬜

   6 units = $ ⬜ × 6

   6 tickets will cost $ ⬜.

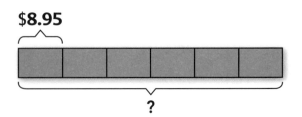

$8.95

?

Exercise 6, pages 81-82

7. Find the value of
   (a) 3600¢ ÷ 6   (b) $36.00 ÷ 6
   (c) 360¢ ÷ 6   (d) $3.60 ÷ 6
   (e) 6300¢ ÷ 9   (f) $63.00 ÷ 9
   (g)   30¢ ÷ 5   (h) $0.30 ÷ 5

8. Estimate, then find the value of $31.10 ÷ 5.

   $30 ÷ 5 = $6

   The value of $31.10 ÷ 5 is about $ ⬜.

   ⬜
   5)$31.10

   The value of $31.10 ÷ 5 is $ ⬜.

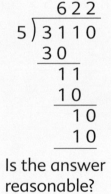

```
      6 2 2
  5 ) 3 1 1 0
      3 0
      1 1
      1 0
        1 0
        1 0
```

Is the answer reasonable?

9. Find the value of $31 ÷ 5.

   ⬜
   5)$31.00

10. Find the value of
    (a) $6.57 ÷ 9   (b) $16.52 ÷ 2   (c) $25 ÷ 4

11. What is the missing number?

    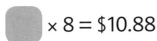 × 8 = $10.88

12. Cindy gave $9.76 to her 4 grandchildren.
    The grandchildren shared the money equally.
    How much did each child receive?

    4 units = $ ⬜

    1 unit = $ ⬜ ÷ 4

    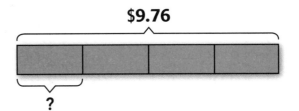

    Each child received $ ⬜ .

13. Mary has $7.23.
    She has three times as much money as Tom.
    How much money does Tom have?

    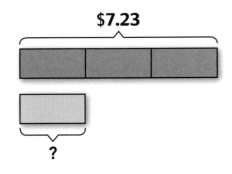

    Tom has $ ⬜ .

Exercise 7, pages 83-84

1. Write in cents.
    (a) $9.99   (b) $83.45   (c) $0.67

2. Write in dollars and cents.
    (a) 652¢   (b) 19¢   (c) 1109¢

3. Multiply. Give your answers in dollars and cents.
    (a) $1.83 × 6   (b) $5.65 × 5   (c) $9.99 × 9
    (d) $7.00 × 8   (e) $0.84 × 4   (f) $0.06 × 3
    (g) $0.20 × 6   (h) $19.54 × 2

4. Divide. Give your answers in dollars and cents.
    (a) $7.11 ÷ 3   (b) $6.39 ÷ 9   (c) $9.68 ÷ 8
    (d) $8.75 ÷ 7   (e) $2.00 ÷ 4   (f) $10.50 ÷ 2
    (g) $9.95 ÷ 5   (h) $3.84 ÷ 6

5. Sam saved $5.21 last week.
    Amy saved twice as much as Sam.
    How much did Amy save?

6. James has $9.38.
    He decides to spend half of this amount and to save the
    other half. How much is he saving?

7. A 5-lb bag of flour cost $2.95. How much is 1 lb of flour?

8. A package of pencils costs $5.45 while a package of erasers
    costs $2.95.
    Mario wants to buy 3 packages of pencils and 1 package
    of erasers. How much does he have to spend?

9. A 5-oz carton of cherries at a farmer's market costs $1.
    Mary wants to buy cherries only if they are less than
    $3 a pound. Should she buy the cherries?

10. An 8-lb bag of oranges costs $10.80.
    Oranges on the fruit stand cost $1.23 a pound.
    Which is a better buy, the 8-lb bag or bagging your
    own oranges?

Find the value of each of the following:

	(a)	(b)	(c)
1.	895 + 5037	6409 + 399	2846 + 754
2.	1436 − 437	3002 − 78	5362 − 26
3.	77 × 4	73 × 9	123 × 5
4.	900 ÷ 2	408 ÷ 3	518 ÷ 8

5. Cameron received $504 for selling pens at $8 each.
   How many pens did he sell?

6. Eric paid $628 for a television set and $1485 for a computer.
   He had $515 left.
   How much money did he have at first?

7. Mrs. Ray bought 4 boxes of apples.
   There were 12 red apples and 8 green apples in each box.
   How many apples were there altogether?

8. Kyle sold 337 boxes of cookies last month.
   He sold 299 more boxes this month than last month.
   How many boxes of cookies did he sell in the two months?

9. Sally bought 200 eggs to make cakes.
   She used 8 eggs to make each cake.

   (a) How many cakes did she make?

   (b) If she sold all the cakes at $10 each, how much money
       would she receive?

Find the value of each of the following:

	(a)	(b)
	(a)	(b)
10.	$14.85 + $26.15	$25.60 − $22.35
11.	$29.65 + $0.95	$41.90 − $16.75
12.	$40.80 + $59.20	$50.00 − $31.05

Find the value of each of the following:

(a)	(b)
13. $34.45 + $28.95	$32.05 − $22.95
14. $72.95 + $26.95	$64.25 − $35.95
15. $2.04 × 7	$8.88 × 8
16. $6.93 ÷ 3	$7.78 ÷ 2

17. A badminton racket costs $15.90.
    A tennis racket costs $42.50.
    How much cheaper is the badminton racket than the tennis racket?

18. The usual price of a radio is $43.
    Its sale price is $29.95.
    How much cheaper is the sale price than the usual price?

19. Rachel saved the same amount each week.
    In 6 weeks, she saved $64.80.
    (a) How much did she save each week?
    (b) Her mother gave her some more money.
         She now has $82.30.
         How much did her mother give her?

20. Mr. Greene bought some vegetables for $2.40 and a fish
    for $3.70.
    He had $21.30 left.
    How much money did he have at first?

21. Wendy bought 3 chickens and a duck.
    1 chicken cost $5.70.
    (a) How much did she spend on the chickens?
    The duck cost $1.95 more than 1 chicken.
    (b) How much did she spend altogether?

Review 9, pages 85-89

10 FRACTIONS

1 Fraction of a Whole

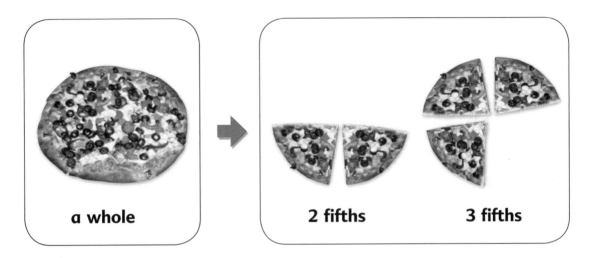

a whole

2 fifths   3 fifths

How many fifths are there in a whole?

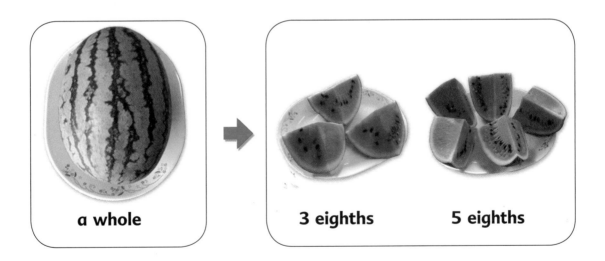

a whole

3 eighths   5 eighths

How many eighths are there in a whole?

1.

(a) $\frac{2}{5}$ of the bar is shaded.

$\frac{2}{5}$ is ⬜ out of the ⬜ equal parts.

$\frac{2}{5}$ = ⬜ fifths

(b) $\frac{3}{5}$ of the bar is **not** shaded.

$\frac{3}{5}$ is ⬜ out of the ⬜ equal parts.

$\frac{3}{5}$ = ⬜ fifths

(c) 1 whole = ⬜ fifths

$1 = \dfrac{\square}{5}$

2.

(a) $\frac{3}{8}$ of the bar is shaded.

⬜ of the bar is **not** shaded.

(b) 1 whole = ⬜ eighths

$1 = \dfrac{\square}{8}$

(c) $\frac{3}{8}$ and ⬜ make 1 whole.

3. What fraction of each shape is shaded?

(a)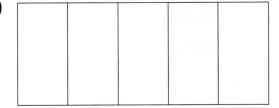

$\frac{1}{5}$

(b)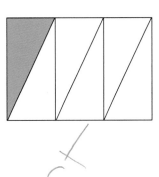

$\frac{1}{6}$

(c)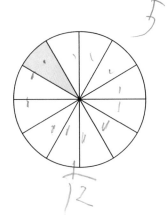

$\frac{1}{12}$

(d)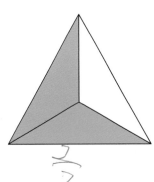

$\frac{2}{3}$

(e)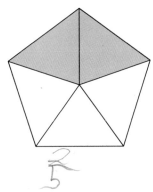

$\frac{2}{5}$

(f)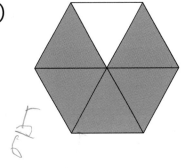

$\frac{5}{6}$

(g)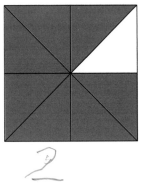

$\frac{5}{8}$

(h)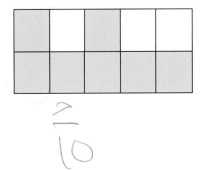

$\frac{7}{10}$

Exercise 1, pages 90-95

4.

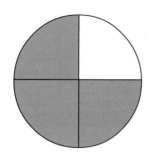

$$\frac{3}{4}$$ ← **numerator**
← **denominator**

In the fraction $\frac{3}{4}$, 3 is the numerator and 4 is the denominator.

Name the numerator and denominator of each of these fractions.

(a) $\frac{2}{5}$ (b) $\frac{4}{10}$ (c) $\frac{6}{7}$ (d) $\frac{6}{9}$

5. Which is greater, $\frac{1}{5}$ or $\frac{1}{3}$?

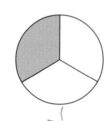

6. Which is greater, $\frac{3}{4}$ or $\frac{3}{5}$?

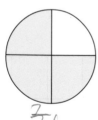
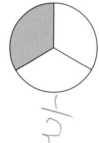

7. Which is greater, $\frac{3}{8}$ or $\frac{5}{8}$?

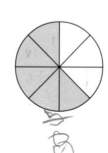

88

It is easy to compare fractions when they have a common numerator or a common denominator.

8.

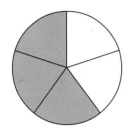 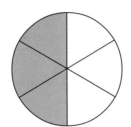 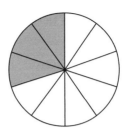

The fractions $\frac{3}{5}$, $\frac{3}{6}$ and $\frac{3}{10}$ have a common numerator.

$3\frac{1}{10}$ is the smallest fraction.

$3\frac{1}{5}$ is the greatest fraction.

9.

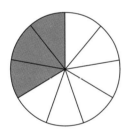 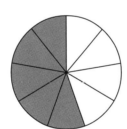 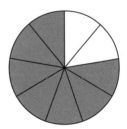

The fractions $\frac{3}{9}$, $\frac{5}{9}$ and $\frac{7}{9}$ have a common denominator.

$\frac{3}{9}$ is the smallest fraction.

$\frac{7}{9}$ is the greatest fraction.

10. Arrange the fractions in order.
Begin with the smallest.

(a) $\frac{1}{5}$, $\frac{1}{7}$, $\frac{1}{3}$

(b) $\frac{2}{7}$, $\frac{2}{3}$, $\frac{2}{9}$

(c) $\frac{5}{8}$, $\frac{7}{8}$, $\frac{4}{8}$

(d) $\frac{5}{12}$, $\frac{9}{12}$, $\frac{4}{12}$

Exercise 2, pages 96-97

1. Find the missing numbers.

    (a) $\frac{1}{4}$ and ▢ make 1 whole.

    (b) $\frac{3}{10}$ and ▢ make 1 whole.

    (c) $\frac{7}{12}$ and ▢ make 1 whole.

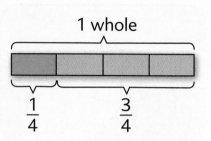

1 whole

$\frac{1}{4}$ $\frac{3}{4}$

2. Name the numerator of each fraction.

    (a) $\frac{2}{3}$ (b) $\frac{6}{10}$ (c) $\frac{9}{12}$

3. Name the denominator of each fraction.

    (a) $\frac{5}{8}$ (b) $\frac{4}{9}$ (c) $\frac{7}{10}$

4. Which fraction is greater?

    (a) $\frac{2}{5}$ or $\frac{4}{5}$ (b) $\frac{1}{4}$ or $\frac{1}{6}$ (c) $\frac{3}{8}$ or $\frac{3}{5}$

5. Which fraction is smaller?

    (a) $\frac{7}{10}$ or $\frac{3}{10}$ (b) $\frac{1}{8}$ or $\frac{1}{10}$ (c) $\frac{2}{9}$ or $\frac{2}{3}$

6. Which is the greatest fraction?

    (a) $\frac{4}{7}$, $\frac{1}{7}$, $\frac{5}{7}$ (b) $\frac{1}{4}$, $\frac{1}{2}$, $\frac{1}{5}$

7. Which is the smallest fraction?

    (a) $\frac{5}{6}$, $\frac{1}{6}$, $\frac{4}{6}$ (b) $\frac{3}{9}$, $\frac{3}{5}$, $\frac{3}{10}$

Exercise 3, pages 98-99

② Equivalent Fractions

Fold a piece of paper into 2 equal parts.
Shade 1 part.

1 out of
2 equal parts.

$\frac{1}{2}$ of the paper is shaded.

Fold the paper again.

2 out of
4 equal parts.

$\frac{2}{4}$ of the paper is shaded.

Fold the paper again.

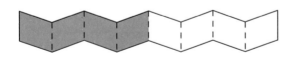

4 out of
8 equal parts.

$\frac{4}{8}$ of the paper is shaded.

The fractions $\frac{1}{2}$, $\frac{2}{4}$ and $\frac{4}{8}$ have different numerators
and denominators.
But they are equal.

$$\frac{1}{2} \qquad = \qquad \frac{2}{4} \qquad = \qquad \frac{4}{8}$$

$\frac{1}{2}, \frac{2}{4}$ and $\frac{4}{8}$ are **equivalent fractions**.

Name some more equivalent fractions of $\frac{1}{2}$.

$\frac{2}{4}$ and $\frac{4}{8}$ are different ways of writing $\frac{1}{2}$.

1.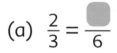

$\frac{2}{3}$ of the bar is shaded.

(a) $\frac{2}{3} = \dfrac{\blacksquare}{6}$

(b) $\frac{2}{3} = \dfrac{\blacksquare}{9}$

(c) $\frac{2}{3} = \dfrac{\blacksquare}{12}$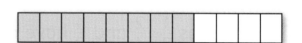

(d) Name some more equivalent fractions of $\frac{2}{3}$.

Exercise 4, pages 100-101

2. What are the missing numerators and denominators?

(a)

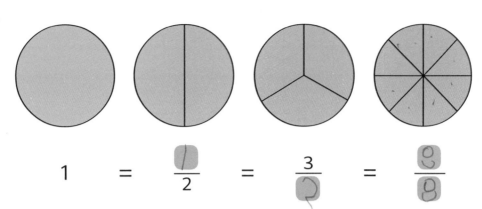

$$1 \quad = \quad \frac{1}{2} \quad = \quad \frac{3}{3} \quad = \quad \frac{8}{8}$$

(b)

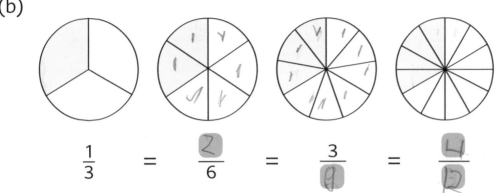

$$\frac{1}{3} \quad = \quad \frac{2}{6} \quad = \quad \frac{3}{9} \quad = \quad \frac{4}{12}$$

To find an equivalent fraction, multiply the numerator and denominator by the same number.

$$\overset{\times 2}{\underset{\times 2}{\frac{1}{3}}} = \frac{\boxed{}}{6} \qquad \overset{\times 3}{\underset{\times 3}{\frac{1}{3}}} = \frac{3}{\boxed{}}$$

3. Find the missing numerator or denominator.

(a) $\frac{1}{4} = \frac{\boxed{}}{12}$ (b) $\frac{2}{3} = \frac{\boxed{}}{9}$ (c) $\frac{1}{5} = \frac{\boxed{}}{10}$

(d) $\frac{1}{6} = \frac{3}{\boxed{}}$ (e) $\frac{3}{5} = \frac{6}{\boxed{}}$ (f) $\frac{3}{4} = \frac{6}{\boxed{}}$

Exercise 5, pages 102-103

4. What are the missing numerators and denominators?

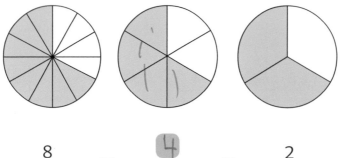

$$\frac{8}{12} = \frac{4}{6} = \frac{2}{3}$$

To find an equivalent fraction, divide the numerator and denominator by the same number.

5. Find the missing numerator or denominator.

(a) $\frac{8}{10} = \frac{\square}{5}$

(b) $\frac{4}{8} = \frac{\square}{2}$

(c) $\frac{6}{9} = \frac{\square}{3}$

(d) $\frac{6}{9} = \frac{2}{\square}$

(e) $\frac{9}{12} = \frac{3}{\square}$

(f) $\frac{10}{12} = \frac{5}{\square}$

Exercise 6, pages 104-105

6. Complete the following equivalent fractions of $\frac{6}{12}$.

(a) $\frac{6}{12} = \frac{3}{\square}$

(b) $\frac{6}{12} = \frac{2}{\square}$

(c) $\frac{6}{12} = \frac{1}{\square}$

The simplest equivalent fraction of $\frac{6}{12}$ is $\frac{\square}{\square}$.

7. Express each of the following fractions in its simplest form.

(a) $\frac{2}{4}$ (b) $\frac{6}{8}$ (c) $\frac{5}{10}$ (d) $\frac{3}{9}$

(e) $\frac{4}{10}$ (f) $\frac{4}{6}$ (g) $\frac{10}{12}$ (h) $\frac{6}{10}$

Exercise 7, pages 106-107

8. Which is greater, $\frac{3}{4}$ or $\frac{5}{8}$?

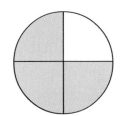 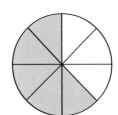

$\frac{3}{4} = \frac{\square}{8}$

9. Which is greater, $\frac{2}{5}$ or $\frac{7}{10}$?

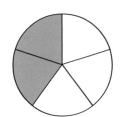 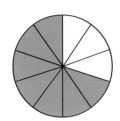

$\frac{2}{5} = \frac{\square}{10}$

10. Which fraction is greater?

(a) $\frac{2}{3}$, $\frac{5}{6}$ (b) $\frac{3}{8}$, $\frac{1}{2}$ (c) $\frac{3}{5}$, $\frac{7}{10}$

11. Which fraction is smaller?

(a) $\frac{4}{5}$, $\frac{7}{10}$ (b) $\frac{11}{12}$, $\frac{5}{6}$ (c) $\frac{2}{3}$, $\frac{5}{9}$

12. Arrange the fractions in order, beginning with the smallest.

(a) $\frac{5}{8}$, $\frac{1}{2}$, $\frac{3}{4}$ (b) $\frac{3}{10}$, $\frac{3}{5}$, $\frac{2}{5}$

Exercise 8, page 108

1. Find the missing numerator in each of the following:

   (a) $\frac{1}{4} = \frac{\blacksquare}{8}$ (b) $\frac{3}{5} = \frac{\blacksquare}{15}$ (c) $\frac{1}{3} = \frac{\blacksquare}{6} = \frac{\blacksquare}{9}$

   (d) $\frac{4}{10} = \frac{\blacksquare}{5}$ (e) $\frac{6}{9} = \frac{\blacksquare}{3}$ (f) $\frac{1}{2} = \frac{\blacksquare}{4} = \frac{\blacksquare}{6}$

2. Find the missing denominator in each of the following:

   (a) $\frac{2}{5} = \frac{4}{\blacksquare}$ (b) $\frac{3}{4} = \frac{9}{\blacksquare}$ (c) $\frac{2}{3} = \frac{4}{\blacksquare} = \frac{6}{\blacksquare}$

   (d) $\frac{6}{12} = \frac{1}{\blacksquare}$ (e) $\frac{6}{8} = \frac{3}{\blacksquare}$ (f) $\frac{1}{2} = \frac{3}{\blacksquare} = \frac{5}{\blacksquare}$

3. Circle the greater fraction.

   (a) $\frac{3}{10}, \frac{7}{10}$ (b) $\frac{5}{6}, \frac{9}{12}$ (c) $\frac{10}{12}, \frac{4}{5}$

   (d) $\frac{1}{2}, \frac{5}{6}$ (e) $\frac{7}{12}, \frac{2}{3}$ (f) $\frac{3}{4}, \frac{5}{8}$

4. Arrange the fractions in order, beginning with the smallest fraction.

   (a) $\frac{3}{7}, \frac{1}{7}, \frac{5}{7}$ (b) $\frac{1}{5}, \frac{1}{2}, \frac{1}{10}$

   (c) $\frac{2}{3}, \frac{1}{2}, \frac{5}{6}$ (d) $\frac{2}{3}, \frac{1}{4}, \frac{5}{12}$

5. Melissa ate $\frac{2}{6}$ of a pie.

   Sara ate $\frac{1}{2}$ of the pie.

   Who ate a bigger portion of the pie?

③ Adding Fractions

Lila drank $\frac{1}{5}$ liter of milk.

Her brother drank $\frac{2}{5}$ liter of milk.

How much milk did they drink altogether?

$\frac{1}{5} + \frac{2}{5} = \boxed{}$

They drank $\boxed{}$ liter of milk altogether.

1 fifth + 2 fifths = 3 fifths

1. Find the sum of $\frac{2}{5}$ and $\frac{3}{5}$.

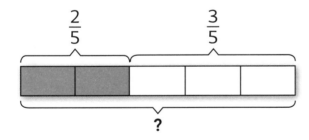

$\frac{2}{5} + \frac{3}{5} = \boxed{}$

2 fifths + 3 fifths = 1 whole

2. (a) Add $\frac{3}{8}$ and $\frac{2}{8}$.

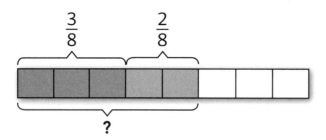

?

$$\frac{3}{8} + \frac{2}{8} = \frac{\boxed{}}{8}$$

(b) Add $\frac{5}{8}$ and $\frac{1}{8}$.

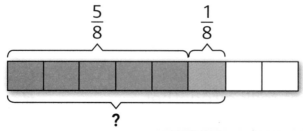

?

Always put the answer
in the simplest form.

$$\frac{5}{8} + \frac{1}{8} = \frac{\boxed{}}{8}$$

$$= \boxed{}$$

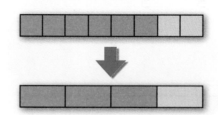

3. Add.

(a) $\frac{1}{9} + \frac{4}{9}$

(b) $\frac{2}{7} + \frac{2}{7}$

(c) $\frac{4}{6} + \frac{1}{6}$

(d) $\frac{1}{6} + \frac{3}{6}$

(e) $\frac{1}{4} + \frac{3}{4}$

(f) $\frac{3}{10} + \frac{5}{10}$

(g) $\frac{3}{7} + \frac{4}{7}$

(h) $\frac{2}{9} + \frac{4}{9}$

(i) $\frac{5}{12} + \frac{1}{12}$

(j) $\frac{2}{5} + \frac{2}{5} + \frac{1}{5}$

(k) $\frac{3}{7} + \frac{3}{7} + \frac{1}{7}$

(l) $\frac{2}{9} + \frac{2}{9} + \frac{2}{9}$

Exercise 9, pages 109-111

4 Subtracting Fractions

Debbie had $\frac{7}{8}$ of a pie.

She ate $\frac{2}{8}$ of the pie.

What fraction of the pie was left?

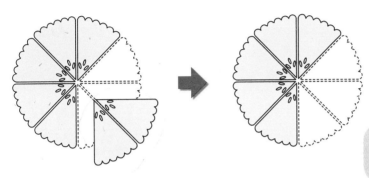

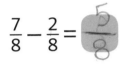

7 eighths — 2 eighths
= 5 eighths

$$\frac{7}{8} - \frac{2}{8} = \boxed{\frac{5}{8}}$$

of the pie was left.

1. Find the difference between $\frac{4}{5}$ and $\frac{3}{5}$.

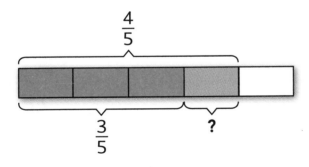

4 fifths — 3 fifths
= 1 fifth

$$\frac{4}{5} - \frac{3}{5} = \boxed{\frac{1}{3}}$$

2. Subtract $\frac{3}{10}$ from 1.

$1 = \frac{10}{10}$

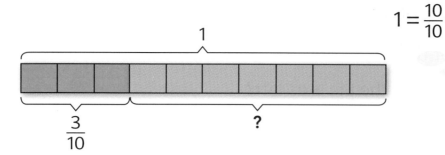

1

$\frac{3}{10}$?

$1 - \frac{3}{10} = \boxed{}$

3. Subtract $\frac{1}{8}$ from $\frac{5}{8}$.

$\frac{5}{8}$

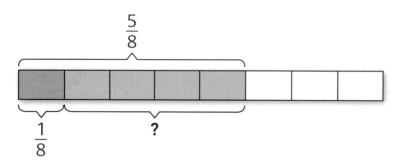

$\frac{1}{8}$?

$\frac{5}{8} - \frac{1}{8} = \dfrac{\boxed{}}{8}$

$= \boxed{}$

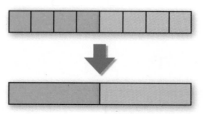

4. Subtract.

(a) $\frac{4}{5} - \frac{1}{5}$

(b) $\frac{6}{8} - \frac{5}{8}$

(c) $\frac{7}{9} - \frac{3}{9}$

(d) $\frac{3}{4} - \frac{1}{4}$

(e) $\frac{7}{10} - \frac{3}{10}$

(f) $\frac{8}{12} - \frac{5}{12}$

(g) $1 - \frac{2}{9}$

(h) $1 - \frac{9}{10}$

(i) $1 - \frac{7}{12}$

(j) $1 - \frac{2}{5} - \frac{2}{5}$

(k) $\frac{7}{8} - \frac{1}{8} - \frac{3}{8}$

(l) $\frac{8}{9} - \frac{1}{9} - \frac{4}{9}$

Exercise 10, pages 112-114

PRACTICE C

Add or subtract.

	(a)	(b)	(c)
1.	$\frac{1}{5} + \frac{3}{5}$	$\frac{2}{6} + \frac{3}{6}$	$\frac{3}{10} + \frac{4}{10}$
2.	$\frac{8}{10} - \frac{5}{10}$	$\frac{5}{7} - \frac{2}{7}$	$1 - \frac{2}{9}$
3.	$\frac{3}{8} + \frac{4}{8}$	$\frac{2}{3} + \frac{1}{3}$	$\frac{2}{9} + \frac{5}{9}$
4.	$1 - \frac{3}{5}$	$\frac{5}{6} - \frac{1}{6}$	$\frac{3}{4} - \frac{1}{4}$
5.	$\frac{3}{10} + \frac{3}{10}$	$\frac{1}{12} + \frac{5}{12}$	$\frac{3}{11} + \frac{5}{11}$

6. Sally ate $\frac{1}{8}$ of a cake and her sister ate $\frac{3}{8}$ of it.
   What fraction of the cake did they eat altogether?

7. Marlon spent $\frac{4}{9}$ of his pocket money and saved the rest.
   What fraction of his pocket money did he save?

8. Mike spent $\frac{3}{7}$ of his money on a book and the rest on a racket.
   What fraction of his money was spent on the racket?

9. Fatimah baked a pie.
   She ate $\frac{1}{6}$ of the pie and gave $\frac{3}{6}$ of the pie to her friends.
   What fraction of the pie did she have left?

5 Fraction of a Set

Part that are dogs   ⟶ $\dfrac{4}{12}$

Total number of animals   ⟶

4 out of 12 animals are dogs.

$\dfrac{4}{12}$ of the animals are dogs.

Part that is dogs   ⟶ $\dfrac{1}{3}$

Number of equal parts   ⟶

1 part out of 3 parts is dogs.

$\dfrac{1}{3}$ of the animals are dogs.

$$\dfrac{4}{12} = \dfrac{1}{3}$$

What fraction of the animals are all white?

1. What fraction of each set is blue?

(a)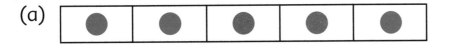

(b)

(c)

(d)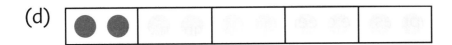

(e)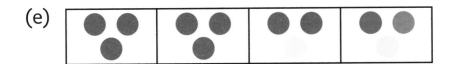

$$\frac{5}{6}$$

2. What fraction of the apples are green?

(a)

(b)

$$\frac{3}{6}$$

$$\frac{2}{6}$$

(c)

(d)

$$\frac{4}{6}$$

3.

(a) What fraction of the apples are green? $\dfrac{6}{10} = \dfrac{3}{5}$

$\dfrac{3}{5}$ of the apples are green.

6 green apples out of 10 apples in total.

(b) $\dfrac{\square}{\square}$ of the apples are red.

$\dfrac{3}{5} + \dfrac{\square}{\square} = 1$ whole (all the apples)

4. What is $\dfrac{1}{3}$ of 9?

$\dfrac{1}{3}$ $\longrightarrow$ 1 part out of
$\phantom{\dfrac{1}{3}}$ $\longrightarrow$ 3 equal parts

Divide 9 into 3 equal groups.

One group is $\dfrac{1}{3}$ of 9.

5. Find $\dfrac{3}{4}$ of 16.

$\dfrac{1}{4}$ of 16 = $\square$

$\dfrac{3}{4}$ of 16 = $\square$

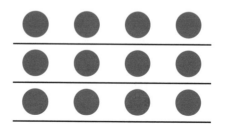

Exercise 11, pages 115-116

6 Fractions and Money

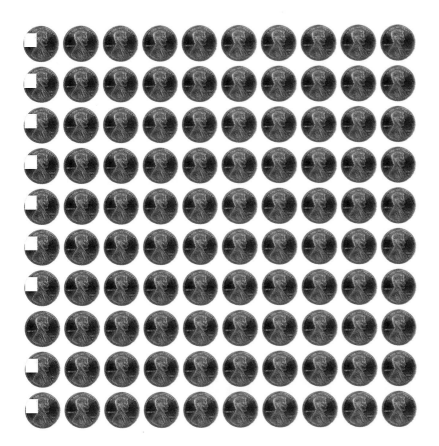

There are 100 pennies in one dollar.

100 pennies = $1.00

1 penny = $0.01

1 penny is $\frac{1}{100}$ of a dollar. $\frac{1}{100}$ of a dollar = $0.01

What fraction of a dollar is 10 pennies?

What fraction of a dollar is 30 pennies?

There are 10 dimes in one dollar.

10 dimes = $1.00

1 dime = $0.10

1 dime is $\frac{1}{10}$ of a dollar. $\frac{1}{10}$ of a dollar = $0.10

3 dimes is $\frac{3}{10}$ of a dollar. $\frac{3}{10}$ of a dollar = $0.30

1. 4 quarters = $

1 quarter = $\frac{1}{4}$ of a dollar

$\frac{1}{4}$ of a dollar = $

2.

2 quarters = $\frac{2}{4}$ of a dollar

$\frac{2}{4} = \frac{1}{2}$

$\frac{1}{2}$ of a dollar = $

3. $\frac{3}{4}$ of a dollar = \$ $\square$

4. What fraction of a dollar is 2 dimes and 1 nickel?

5. \$0.10 = $\frac{1}{10}$ of a dollar

   \$0.30 = $\frac{3}{10}$ of a dollar

   \$0.70 = $\frac{\square}{10}$ of a dollar

6. What fraction of a dollar is 5 dimes?

7. What fraction of a dollar is a quarter, 2 dimes, and a nickel?

8. What fraction of a dollar is 25 pennies?

Exercise 12, page 117

1.

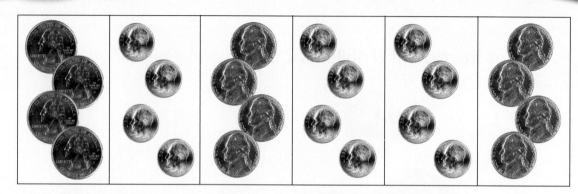

   (a) How many coins are there? ☐

   (b) $\dfrac{\square}{\square}$ of the coins are quarters.

   (c) $\dfrac{\square}{\square}$ of the coins are dimes.

   (d) $\dfrac{\square}{\square}$ of the coins are nickels.

2. Write each amount of money as a fraction of a dollar.
    (a) $0.25   (b) $0.50   (c) $0.10
    (d) $0.75   (e) $0.30   (f) $1.00

3. Colleen has 8 nickels.
    What fraction of a dollar does she have?

4. Sam has 1 quarter, 3 dimes, and 3 nickels.
    (a) What fraction of his coins are quarters?
    (b) What fraction of his coins are dimes?
    (c) What fraction of his coins are nickels?
    (d) How much money does he have?
    (e) What fraction of a dollar does he have?

1. Write the numbers.

    (a) nine thousand, two hundred ten

    (b) four thousand, sixty

2. Write the numbers in words.

    (a) 6204   (b) 3540   (c) 5028

3. What number is 100 less than 4000?

4. Write the numbers in order, beginning with the smallest.

    (a) 4104, 4014, 4041, 4410

    (b) 2211, 1112, 2111, 2121

5. Find the product of 125 and 8.

6. Find the quotient and remainder when 500 is divided by 8.

7. What number must be subtracted from 55 to give the answer 44?

8. (a) How many $10 bills can you get for $200?

    (b) How many nickels can you get for $1.50?

9   Find the missing numerator or denominator.

    (a) $\frac{1}{4} = \frac{\square}{12}$ (b) $\frac{2}{3} = \frac{6}{\square}$ (c) $\frac{8}{10} = \frac{4}{\square}$

10. Circle the smaller fraction.

    (a) $\frac{1}{3}$, $\frac{1}{4}$ (b) $\frac{2}{7}$, $\frac{4}{7}$ (c) $\frac{10}{10}$, $\frac{11}{12}$

    (d) $\frac{3}{4}$, $\frac{5}{8}$ (e) $\frac{2}{5}$, $\frac{3}{10}$ (f) $\frac{3}{6}$, $\frac{2}{3}$

11. Find the missing numbers.

(a) 4 m 20 cm = ☐ cm   (b) 205 cm = ☐ m ☐ cm

(c) 2 km 95 m = ☐ m   (d) 1600 m = ☐ km ☐ m

(e) 1 kg 40 g = ☐ g   (f) 2450 g = ☐ kg ☐ g

(g) 3 ℓ 60 ml = ☐ ml   (h) 2525 ml = ☐ ℓ ☐ ml

(i) 10 yd 2 ft = ☐ ft   (j) 17 in. = ☐ ft ☐ in.

(k) 8 lb 10 oz = ☐ oz   (l) 18 oz = ☐ lb ☐ oz

(m) 12 qt 1 pt = ☐ pt   (n) 15 c = ☐ pt ☐ c

12. John bought 6 pounds of pears.
He gave the cashier $10.
How much change did he receive?

PEARS
70¢ for 1 lb

13. A badminton racket costs $9.60.
A tennis racket costs $38.40.
How much more is the cost of the tennis racket than the cost of the badminton racket?

14. A tub contains 1 liter of yogurt.
Peter and his friends eat 325 ml of it.
How much yogurt is left?

15. Sally bought 10 cartons of milk.
Each carton contained 125 ml of milk.
Find the total amount of milk in liters and milliliters.

16. Juan spent $\frac{4}{9}$ of his allowance and saved the rest.
What fraction of his allowance did he save?

17. Matthew spent $\frac{3}{7}$ of his money on a book and the rest on a racket.
What fraction of his money was spent on the racket?

18. Aimee wants to donate money to a food bank.

She plans to give $\frac{1}{4}$ of every dollar she makes babysitting to the food bank.

   (a) How much money from every dollar does she donate?
   (b) She makes $8 babysitting.
        How much money does she donate?

19.

Jessica is going to pick a ball from the box without looking.
   (a) Is it certain she will get a ball from the box?
   (b) Is it likely that she will get a green ball?
   (c) Is it certain that she will get a green ball?
   (d) Is it unlikely that she will get a red ball?
   (e) Is it impossible for her to get a white ball?
   (f) Is it impossible for her to get a yellow ball?

Review 10, pages 118-122

11 TIME

1 Hours and Minutes

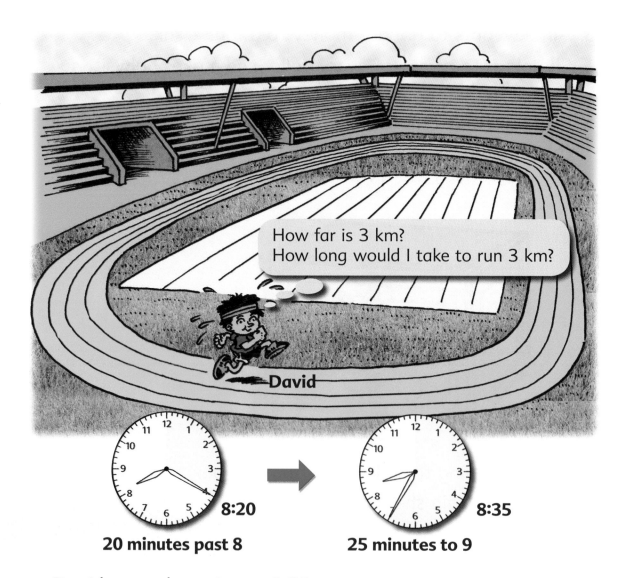

How far is 3 km?
How long would I take to run 3 km?

David

8:20
20 minutes past 8

8:35
25 minutes to 9

David started running at 8:20 a.m.
He ran 3 km.
He finished at 8:35 a.m.
He took 15 minutes to run 3 km.

We read 8:20 as **eight twenty**.
8:20 is 20 minutes after 8 o'clock. We say the time is twenty minutes past eight.

We read 8:35 as **eight thirty-five**.
8:35 is 25 minutes before 9 o'clock. We say the time is twenty-five minutes to nine.

1. Find out how many times you can write your name in 1 minute.

2. What time is it?

(a)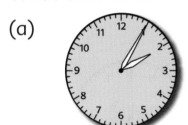

(b)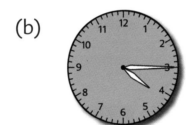

(c)

(d)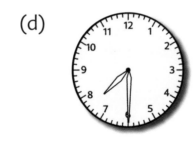

(e)

(f)

Exercise 1, pages 123-124

a.m. means after 12:00 midnight and before 12:00 noon.
p.m. means after 12:00 noon and before 12:00 midnight.

3. What time is 26 minutes after 9:30 a.m.?

26 minutes later

4. How many minutes are there in **1 hour**?

1 hour later

1 hour later

5. (a) How many **minutes** are there from 1:15 p.m. to 1:42 p.m.?

(b) How many **hours** are there from 3:18 p.m. to 8:18 p.m.?

(c) How long is it from 9:15 a.m. to 11:30 a.m.?

(d) How long is it from 10:45 a.m. to 1:15 p.m.?

The **hour (h)** and **minute (min)** are units of time.

1 hour = 60 minutes

Exercise 2, pages 125-126

6. The table shows the time taken
   by three children to paint a picture.

   (a) Who took the longest time?
   (b) Who took the shortest time?

Name	Time taken
Amy	1 h 15 min
Jane	2 h 5 min
Sue	1 h 20 min

7. Marcus took 1 h 35 min to complete a jigsaw puzzle.
   Write the time taken in minutes.

   1 h 35 min = ⬜ min

   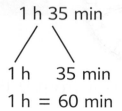

   1 h 35 min
   1 h   35 min
   1 h = 60 min

8. Write in minutes.
   (a) 2 h   (b) 2 h 10 min   (c) 2 h 45 min
   (d) 3 h   (e) 3 h 5 min   (f) 3 h 15 min

9. Mrs. Lean sewed 4 sets of curtains.
   She took 50 minutes to sew each set of curtains.
   Find the total time taken in hours and minutes.

   50 min × 4 = 200 min

   200 min = ⬜ h ⬜ min

   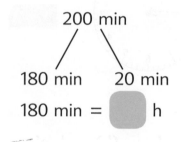

   200 min
   180 min   20 min
   180 min = ⬜ h

10. Write in hours and minutes.
    (a) 70 min   (b) 85 min   (c) 100 min
    (d) 125 min   (e) 160 min   (f) 210 min

Exercise 3, pages 127-128

11. A plane left San Francisco at 8:00 a.m.
    It arrived in Portland at 9:05 a.m.
    How long did the journey take?

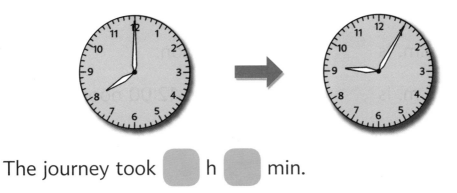

The journey took ☐ h ☐ min.

12. Kristi went to the market at 7:15 a.m.
    She came home 1 h 45 min later.
    When did she come home?

What time is
1 h 45 min
after 7:15 a.m.?

She came home at ☐ a.m.

13. Sally took 1 h 10 min to do her homework.
    She finished doing her homework at 9:40 p.m.
    When did she start?

What time is
1 h 10 min
before 9:40 p.m.?

She started at ☐ p.m.

Exercise 4, pages 129-130

14.

10:45 a.m. 12:00 noon   2:00 p.m.   3:30 p.m.

(a) 2:00 p.m. is ⬚ h after 12:00 noon.

(b) 3:30 p.m. is ⬚ h ⬚ min after 12:00 noon.

(c) 10:45 a.m. is ⬚ h ⬚ min before 12:00 noon.

15. A supermarket is open from 10:15 a.m. to 9:30 p.m. every day.
How long is the supermarket open a day?

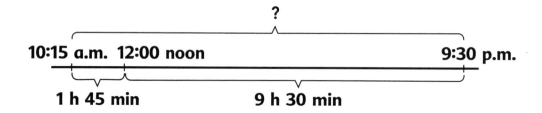

?

10:15 a.m. 12:00 noon   9:30 p.m.

1 h 45 min   9 h 30 min

1 h 45 min $\xrightarrow{+9\,h}$ 10 h 45 min $\xrightarrow{+30\,min}$ 11 h 15 min

1 h 45 min + 9 h 30 min = ⬚ h ⬚ min

The supermarket is open ⬚ h ⬚ min a day.

16.

9:10 p.m.   12:00 midnight   4:00 a.m.   6:40 a.m.

(a) 4:00 a.m. is ⬜ h after 12:00 midnight.

(b) 6:40 a.m. is ⬜ h ⬜ min after 12:00 midnight.

(c) 9:10 p.m. is ⬜ h ⬜ min before 12:00 midnight.

17. A night tour began at 10:30 p.m. and lasted 3 h 20 min.
    When did the night tour end?

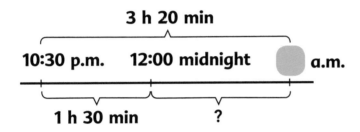

$$3 \text{ h } 20 \text{ min} \xrightarrow{-1\text{h}} 2 \text{ h } 20 \text{ min} \xrightarrow{-30\text{ min}} 1 \text{ h } 50 \text{ min}$$

3 h 20 min − 1 h 30 min = ⬜ h ⬜ min

The night tour ended at ⬜ a.m.

18. Add or subtract.
    (a) 2 h 40 min + 3 h   (b) 2 h 20 min + 45 min
    (c) 3 h 15 min − 2 h   (d) 3 h 5 min − 30 min
    (e) 1 h 25 min + 2 h 15 min   (f) 2 h 40 min + 2 h 25 min
    (g) 3 h 50 min − 1 h 35 min   (h) 3 h 20 min + 1 h 40 min

Exercise 5, pages 131-132

PRACTICE A

1. Add or subtract.

   (a) 1 h 45 min + 2 h   (b) 3 h 40 min − 2 h

   (c) 2 h 15 min + 45 min   (d) 3 h − 1 h 45 min

   (e) 1 h 30 min + 1 h 50 min (f) 2 h 10 min − 1 h 30 min

2. This clock is 5 minutes slow.
   What is the correct time?

3. How long is it?

   (a) From 4:40 a.m. to 11:55 a.m.

   (b) From 5:45 p.m. to 7:00 p.m.

   (c) From 10:05 p.m. to 12:00 midnight.

   (d) From 2:40 p.m. to 3:25 p.m.

4. David took 2 h 35 min to repair a van and 1 h 55 min to repair a car.

   (a) How long did he take to repair both vehicles?

   (b) How much longer did he take to repair the van than the car?

5. Cameron took 2 h 30 min to paint his room.
   He began at 9:20 a.m.
   What time did he finish painting his room?

6. A group of children left for a field trip at 8:30 a.m.
   They returned 4 h 10 min later.
   What time did they return?

7. A supermarket opens for business at 9:30 a.m.
   Its workers have to report for work 40 minutes earlier.
   What time must the workers report for work?

2 Other Units of Time

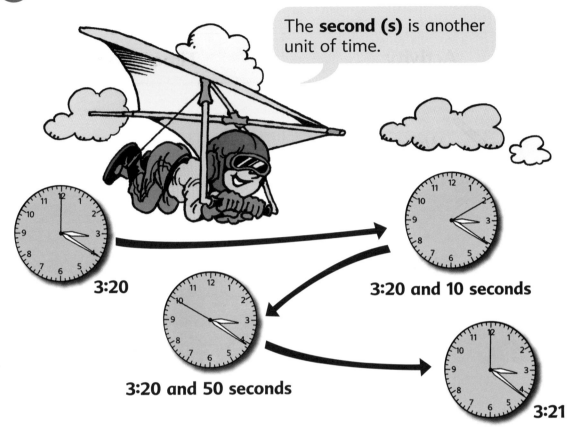

The **second (s)** is another unit of time.

3:20

3:20 and 10 seconds

3:20 and 50 seconds

3:21

1 minute = 60 seconds

1. (a) Find out how many times you can skip in 10 seconds.

(b) How long do you take to write the word CHILDREN?
(c) How long do you take to run 100 m?

2. Use a stopwatch.
   Measure the time taken for each of the following activities.

Activity	Time taken
Write the words SING A SONG.	seconds
Walk 10 steps.	seconds
Draw 5 triangles.	seconds
Skip 15 times.	seconds
Run 100 meters.	seconds

The hour (h), minute (min) and second (s) are units of time.

1 h = 60 min
1 min = 60 s

3. (a) Write 3 min 40 s in seconds.

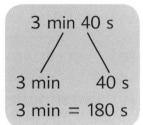

3 min 40 s
3 min   40 s
3 min = 180 s

3 min 40 s = ▢ s

(b) Write 150 s in minutes and seconds.

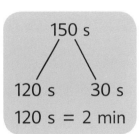

150 s
120 s   30 s
120 s = 2 min

150 s = ▢ min ▢ s

Exercise 6, pages 133-136

4. (a) 1 year = ▢ months

(b) 2 years = ▢ months

The **year**, **month**, **week** and **day** are units of time too.

(c) 2 years 4 months = ▢ months

(d) 40 months = ▢ years ▢ months

5. (a) 1 week = ▢ days

(b) 3 week = ▢ days

Exercise 7, pages 137-138

(c) 3 weeks 4 days = ▢ days

(d) 30 days = ▢ weeks ▢ days

Exercise 8, pages 139-140

1. Find the missing numbers.

   (a) 2 h 12 min = ▢ min   (b) 108 min = ▢ h ▢ min

   (c) 2 min 3 s = ▢ s   (d) 94 s = ▢ min ▢ s

   (e) 1 year 9 months = ▢ months

   (f) 30 months = ▢ years ▢ months

   (g) 2 weeks 5 days = ▢ days

   (h) 40 days = ▢ weeks ▢ days

2. The flying time from Chicago to Minneapolis is 1 h 35 min and from Chicago to Miami is 3 h 15 min.
   How much longer does it take to fly to Miami than to Minneapolis?

3. A bookshop is open from 9:30 a.m. to 5:00 p.m.
   How long is the bookshop open?

4. Molly went shopping at 10:20 a.m.
   She returned home 4 hours later.
   When did she return home?

5. Coby completed a jigsaw puzzle in 1 h 6 min.
   Lily completed the same jigsaw puzzle 10 minutes faster.
   How long did Lily take to complete the jigsaw puzzle?

6. Larry and his family went to the park for a picnic.
   They left home at 8:30 a.m. and arrived at the park at 9:15 a.m.
   How long did the journey take?

7. Mr. Coles took 8 h 45 min to drive from Los Angeles to San Francisco.
   He arrived there at 2:15 p.m.
   What time did he leave Los Angeles?

1. What time is it?
    (a) 8 h 55 min after 12:00 noon
    (b) 1 h 30 min after 12:00 midnight

2. Write the missing numerator or denominator.

    (a)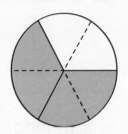

    (b)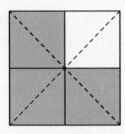

    (c)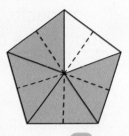

    (a) $\frac{2}{3} = \frac{\square}{6}$

    (b) $\frac{3}{4} = \frac{6}{\square}$

    (c) $\frac{4}{5} = \frac{\square}{10}$

3. What fraction of each set of fish is striped?
    Give each answer in its simplest form.

    (a)

    (b)

4. Mr. Chen stayed in Japan for 19 months.
    Mr. Lee stayed there for 2 years 4 months.
    Who stayed longer?
    How many months longer?

5. A machine can fill 140 jars of jam in 10 minutes.
   How many jars can it fill in 1 minute?

6. An art lesson started at 5:40 p.m.
   It lasted 45 minutes.
   When did the lesson end?

7. A tank can hold 10 times as much water as a bucket.
   The capacity of the tank is 60 liters.
   What is the capacity of the bucket?

8. A ribbon 1 m long is cut into three pieces.

   One piece is $\frac{5}{8}$ m long. The second piece is $\frac{2}{8}$ m long.

   What is the length of the third piece?

9. Adam bought a toothbrush and a tube of toothpaste.
   The toothbrush cost $6.50.
   The tube of toothpaste cost $1.80.
   How much did he pay altogether?

10. Tyler had a box of mangoes.
    After giving 3 mangoes each to
    16 children, he had 20 mangoes left.
    How many mangoes were there in the
    box at first?

11. Juanita spent $4.80 on strings and $2.50 on beads to
    make a flowerpot hanger.
    How much did it cost her to make a flowerpot hanger?

12. Mrs. Chavez bought 8 towels.
    She gave the cashier $40 and received $7.60 in change.
    (a) How much did she pay for the towels?
    (b) What was the cost of 1 towel?

Review 11, pages 141-145

12 GEOMETRY

1 Angles

Use two cards to form an **angle** like this:

Then make a bigger angle.
What is the biggest angle you can get?
Compare it with your friends'.

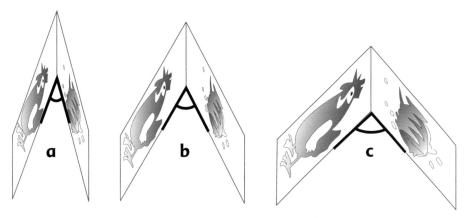

Which angle is the smallest?
Which angle is the biggest?

1. Here are some examples of angles.

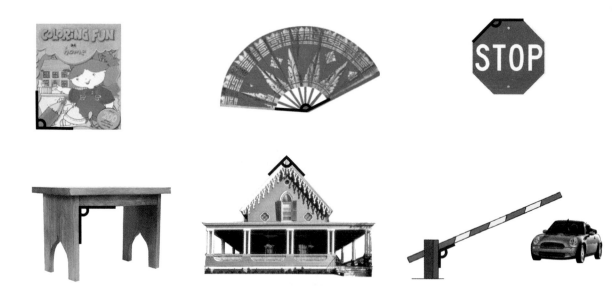

Look for some more angles around you.

2. Any two sides of a triangle make an angle.

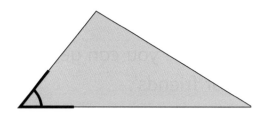

A triangle has ⬜ sides and ⬜ angles.

3. Here are some 4-sided figures.
How many angles does each figure have?

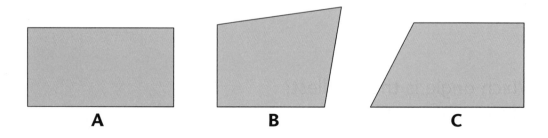

A   B   C

4. Which of these figures are polygons?

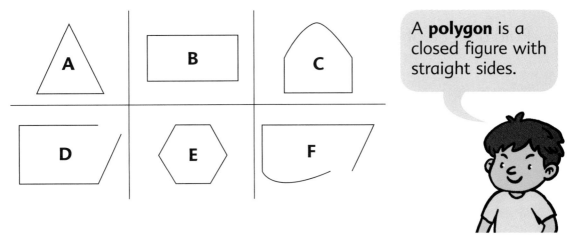

A **polygon** is a closed figure with straight sides.

5. How many angles and sides does each of these polygons have?

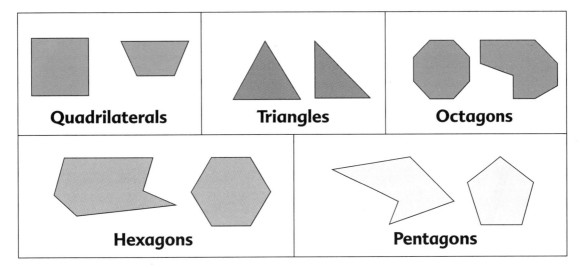

| Quadrilaterals | Triangles | Octagons |
| Hexagons | | Pentagons |

6. Name each of these polygons.

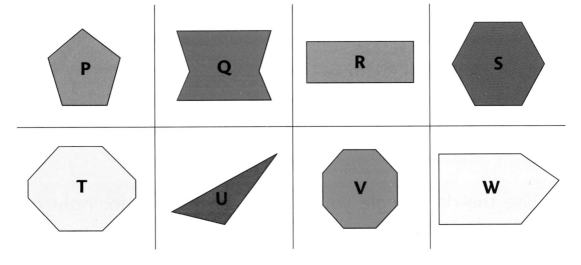

Exercise 1, pages 146-147

② Right Angles

Fold a piece of paper twice to make an angle like this:

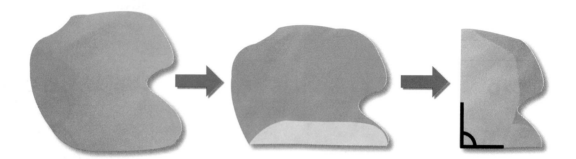

The angle you have made is a special one.
It is a **right angle**.
Use the right angle you have made to find out which of
the following angles are right angles.

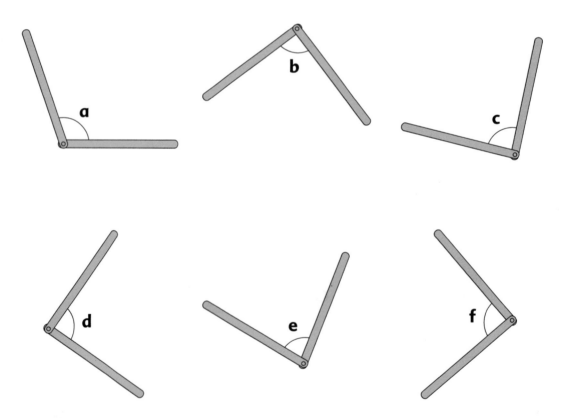

Use the right angle you have made to look for right angles
around you.

1. How many right angles can you find in
   (a) a square?   (b) a rectangle?

2. Which one of these triangles has a right angle?
   Which one has an angle which is **greater than** a right angle?

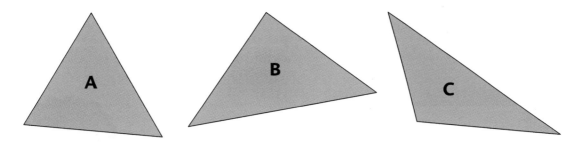

3. How many angles does each of these figures have?
   How many are right angles?

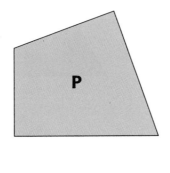
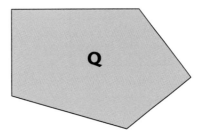
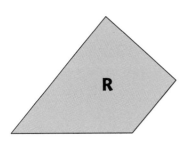
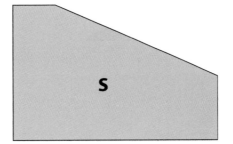

Exercise 2, pages 148-150

3 Quadrilaterals and Triangles

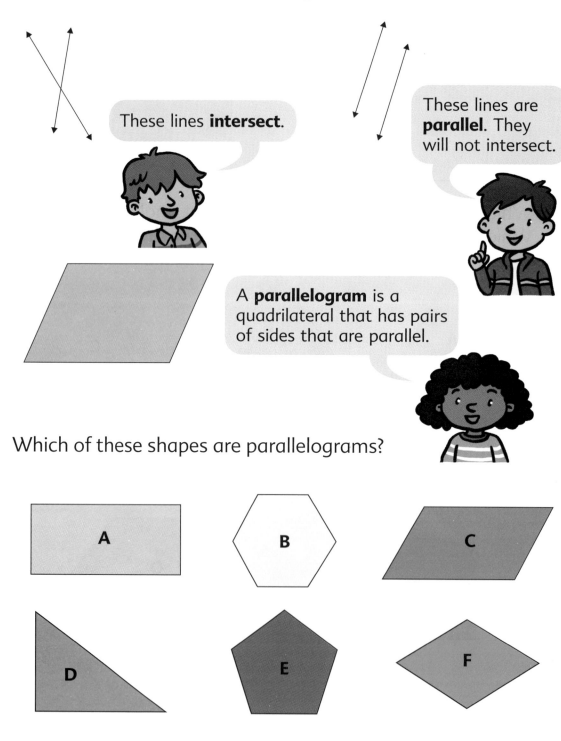

These lines **intersect**.

These lines are **parallel**. They will not intersect.

A **parallelogram** is a quadrilateral that has pairs of sides that are parallel.

Which of these shapes are parallelograms?

A

B

C

D

E

F

1. Is this a parallelogram?

A **rhombus** is a parallelogram with 4 equal sides.

2. Is a square a parallelogram?

   Is a square a rhombus?

3. Is a rectangle a parallelogram?

   Is a rectangle a rhombus?

4.

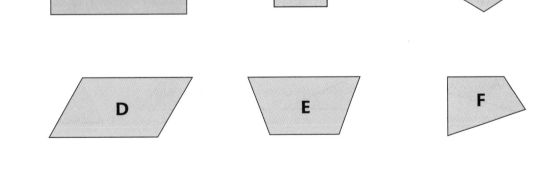

   (a) Which quadrilaterals have 2 pairs of parallel sides?
   (b) Which quadrilaterals have 2 pairs of equal sides?
   (c) Which quadrilaterals have 2 or more right angles?

5. Can a triangle have parallel sides?

6.

  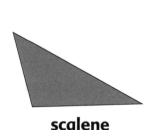

equilateral   **isosceles**   **scalene**

An equilateral triangle is also an isosceles triangle.

(a) Which triangle has no equal sides?
(b) Which triangle has 2 equal sides?
(c) Which triangle has 3 equal sides?

A **right triangle** is a triangle with a right angle.
Can a triangle have 2 right angles?

7.

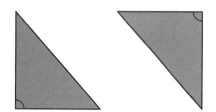  

(a) Can a right triangle be scalene?
(b) Can a right triangle be isosceles?
(c) Can a right triangle be equilateral?

8.

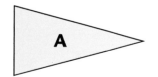   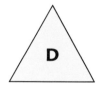

(a) Which triangles are equilateral?
(b) Which triangles are isosceles?
(c) Which triangles are scalene?
(d) Which triangles are right triangles?

Exercise 3, pages 151-152

4 Solid figures

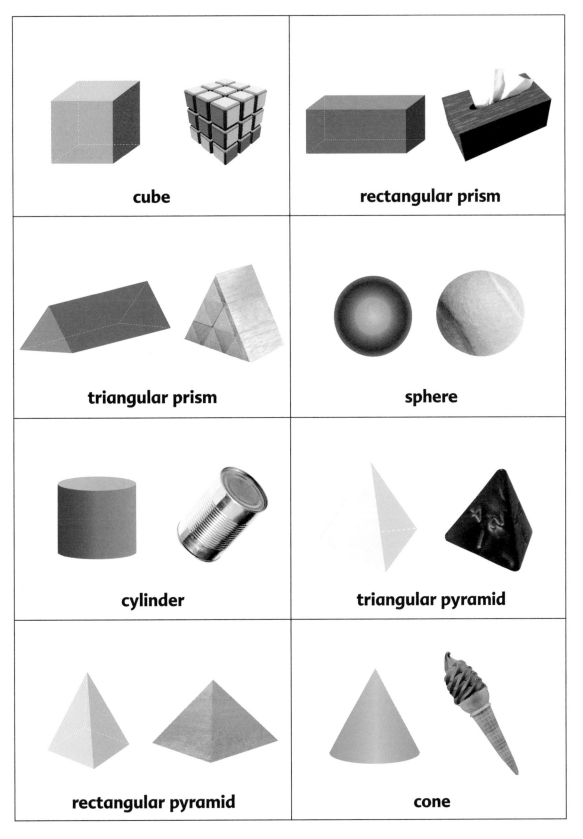

cube

rectangular prism

triangular prism

sphere

cylinder

triangular pyramid

rectangular pyramid

cone

The vertex is the corner of a solid.

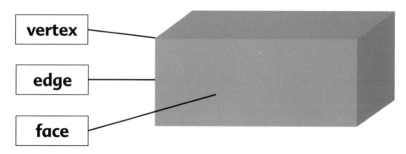

vertex

edge

face

A rectangular prism has 6 faces, 12 edges, and 8 vertices.

How many edges does a square pyramid have?

How many vertices?

How many faces does a sphere have?

1. Name the solids that are used to make each object.

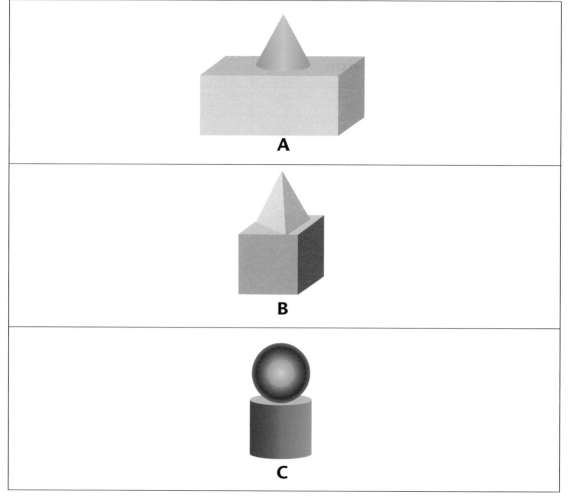

A

B

C

Exercise 4, pages 153-154

1. Arrange the fractions in order, beginning with the smallest.

   (a) $\dfrac{3}{4}, \dfrac{1}{2}, \dfrac{5}{8}$

   (b) $\dfrac{1}{2}, \dfrac{3}{5}, \dfrac{3}{10}$

2. Each side of a triangle is 9 cm long.
   What is the total length of all the sides?

3. (a) $3 \times 4 \times 9 = 9 \times 4 \times \boxed{}$

   (b) $7 \times 6 = 35 + \boxed{}$

   (c) $4500 + 100 = \boxed{} - 100$

   (d) $560 + 80 = 600 + \boxed{}$

   (e) $\dfrac{3}{10} + \boxed{} = \dfrac{7}{10}$

   (f) $1 - \dfrac{1}{6} = \dfrac{3}{6} + \boxed{}$

4. Tom bought a wire and cut it into 8 pieces.
   Each piece of wire was 30 cm long.
   Find the length of the wire he bought.
   Give the answer in meters and centimeters.

5. 2500 people were at a show.
   1360 of them were men.
   240 were children.
   The rest were women.
   (a) How many women were there?
   (b) How many more adults than children were there?

6. Nicole made 286 cookies.
   She gave away 30 cookies and sold the rest at $1 for 8.
   How much money did she receive?

7. (a) How many sides and angles does a hexagon have?

   (b) How many equal sides does an equilateral triangle have?

   (c) How many right angles does a rectangle have?

8. Anna, Peter and John shared a pizza.

   Anna and Peter each received $\frac{1}{5}$ of the pizza.

   What fraction of the pizza did John receive?

9.

580 m

Park

Library

?

Tom's house

   Tom's house is 1 km from the park.
   How far is Tom's house from the library?

10. (a) What is the total weight of the
    3 sticks of butter and the bag of flour?

    (b) If each stick of butter weighs
    300 g, find the weight of the bag of
    flour in kilograms and grams.

11.

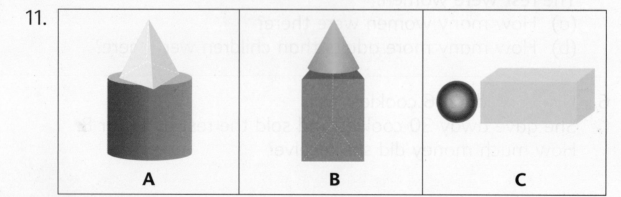

| A | B | C |

   (a) Which figures contain pyramids?

   (b) Which figures contain prisms?

Review 12, pages 155-158

13 AREA, PERIMETER AND VOLUME

1 Area

These shapes are made up of the same number of square tiles.

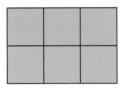 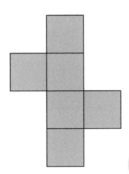 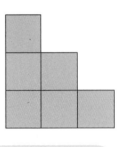

Each tile is 1 square unit.

The shapes are of the same size.
They have the same **area**.
The area of each shape is  square units.

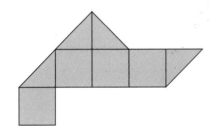 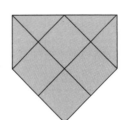 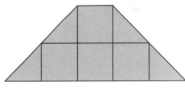

Each ■ is 1 square unit.

Each ◢ is $\frac{1}{2}$ square unit.

These figures have the same area.

The area of each figure is square units.

1. (a)

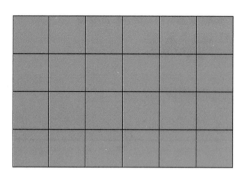

The area of the shape is [ ] square units.

(b)

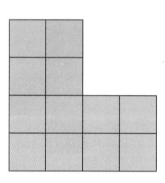

The area of the shape is [ ] square units.

(c)

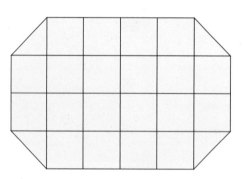

The area of the shape is [ ] square units.

2. What is the area of each of the following figures?

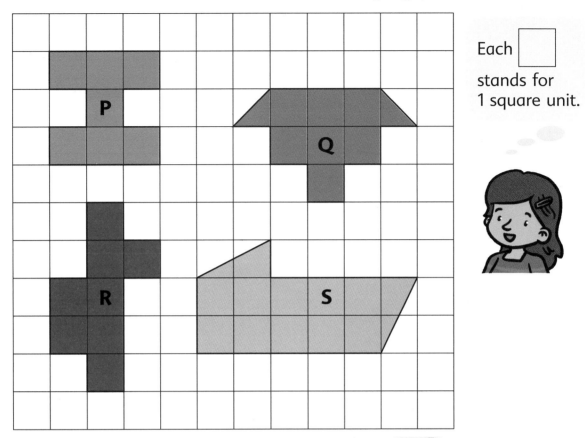

Each ▢ stands for 1 square unit.

Exercise 1, pages 159-162

3. Use square cards to make these shapes.

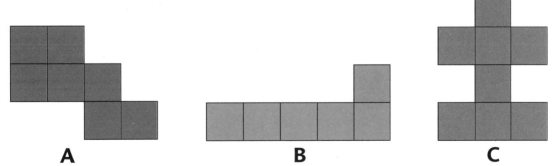

A   B   C

The area of Shape A is ▢ square units.

The area of Shape B is ▢ square units.

The area of Shape C is ▢ square units.

Which shape is the biggest?
Which shape is the smallest?

4. What is the area of each of the following figures?

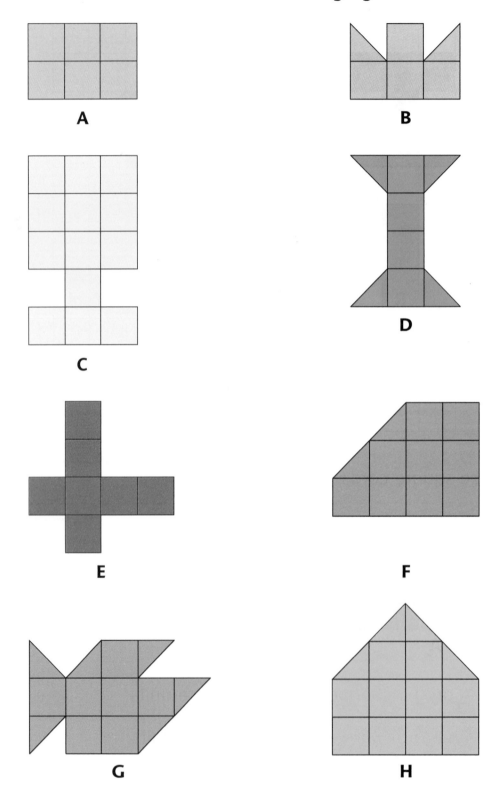

A

B

C

D

E

F

G

H

Which figure has the smallest area?
Which figure has the greatest area?

5. Which two shapes are of the same size?

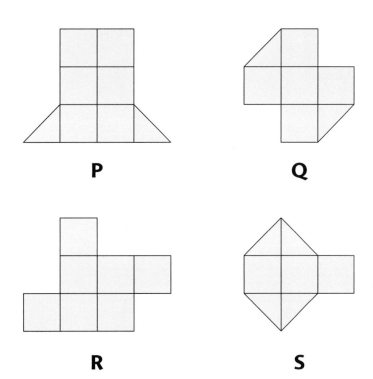

P   Q

R   S

6. How many of these  will cover the inside of each of the following figures?

(a)    (b)

Exercise 2, pages 163-166

7. This is a 1-cm square.

1 cm

1 cm

Each side of the square is 1 cm long.

Its area is 1 **square centimeter**.

Give the area of each of the following squares in square centimeters.

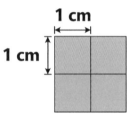

1 cm

1 cm

a 2-cm square

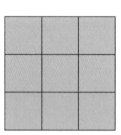

a 3-cm square

a 4-cm square

The square centimeter is a unit of area.

A 2-cm square is made up of 4 pieces of 1-cm squares. Its area is 4 square centimeters.

8. (a) What is the area of a 5-cm square?
   (b) What is the area of a 10-cm square?

9. This figure is made up of 1-cm squares.
   Find its area.

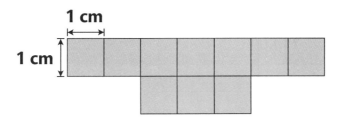

10. What is the area of each of the following figures?

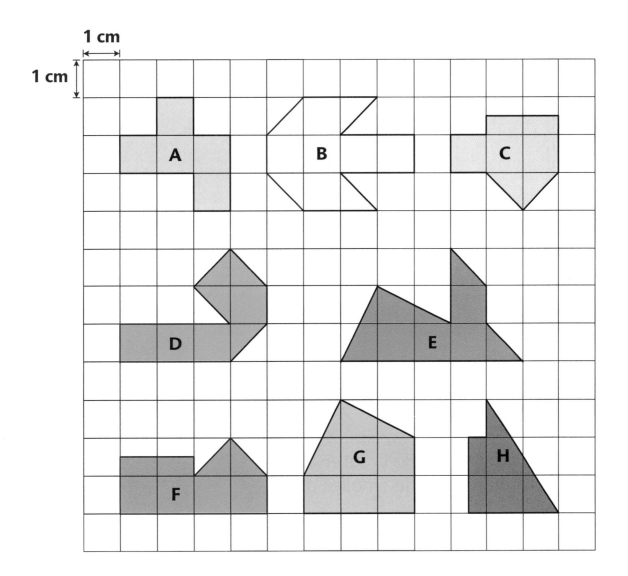

11. Each side of this square is 1 inch long.

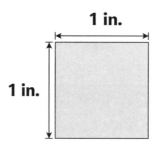

1 in.

1 in.

Its area is 1 **square inch**.

The square inch is also a unit of area.

Give the area of each of the following figures in square inches.

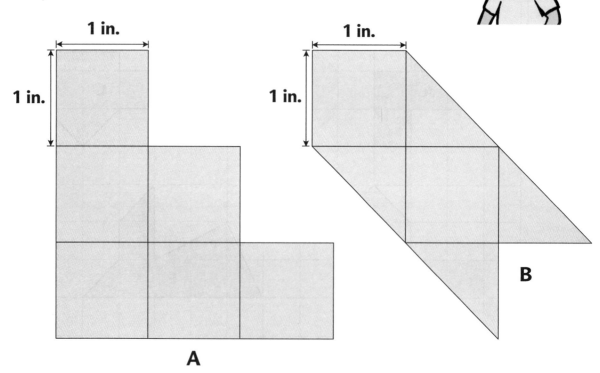

Which figure has the greater area?
Which figure has the smaller area?

Exercise 3, pages 167-169

② Perimeter

Sue used 3 pieces of wire of the same length to make the triangle, the square and the rectangle.

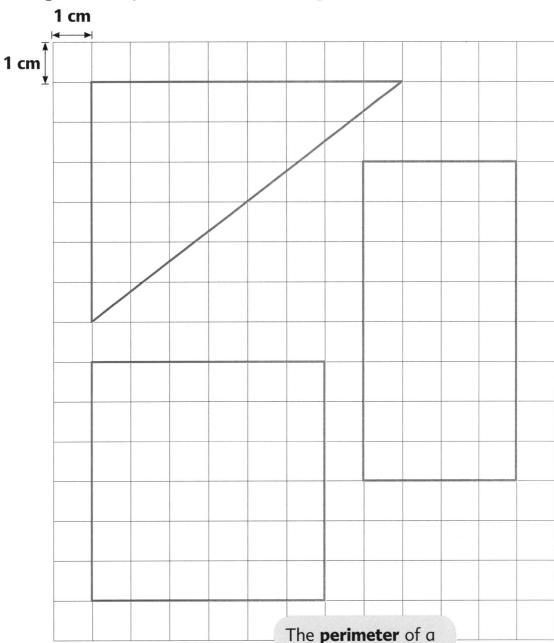

The **perimeter** of a figure is the distance around the figure.

They have the same perimeter.
The perimeter of each figure is cm.

1. Measure with thread, the perimeter of each of these figures.

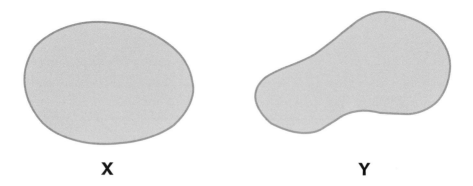

X   Y

Which figure has a longer perimeter?

2. (a) Measure the perimeter of your textbook in centimeters.
   (b) Measure the perimeter of your classroom in meters.

3. These two figures are made up of the same number of 1-cm squares.

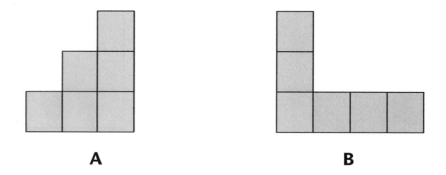

A   B

(a) They have the same area.

The area of each figure is ⬚ square centimeters.

(b) They have different perimeters.

The perimeter of Figure A is ⬚ cm.

The perimeter of Figure B is ⬚ cm.

4. These figures are made up of 1-cm squares.

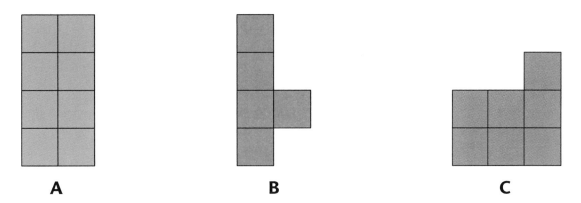

A B C

(a) Do they have the same area?

(b) Do they have the same perimeter?

5. These figures are made up of 1-cm squares.

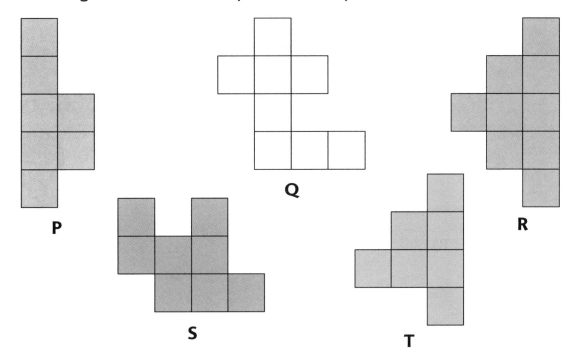

P Q R S T

(a) Which two figures have the same area but different perimeters?

(b) Which two figures have the same perimeter but different areas?

(c) Which two figures have the same area and perimeter?

6. (a) Each side of the square is 6 cm long.
Find its perimeter.

Perimeter = 6 + 6 + 6 + 6

= ⬜ cm

6 cm

6 cm

(b) The length of the rectangle is 12 cm.
Its width is 4 cm.
Find its perimeter.

Perimeter = 12 + 4 + 12 + 4

= ⬜ cm

4 cm

12 cm

7. Find the perimeter of each of the following figures:

When we draw figures, we can make them smaller than the actual size. We label the sides with the actual sizes.

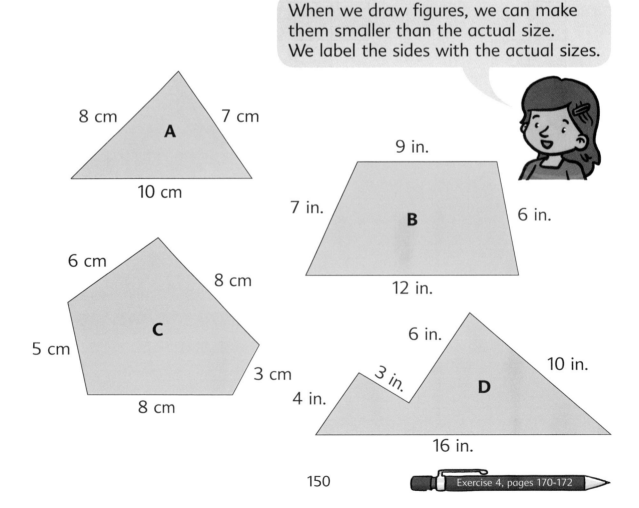

8 cm   A   7 cm

10 cm

9 in.

7 in.   B   6 in.

12 in.

6 cm

8 cm

C

5 cm

8 cm

3 cm

4 in.

6 in.

3 in.

D   10 in.

16 in.

150

Exercise 4, pages 170-172

③ Volume

The drawing of a cube is shown below.

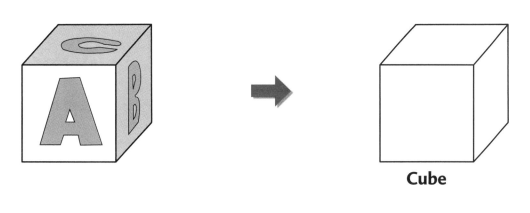

Cube

We can draw a cube in other ways.

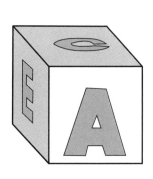 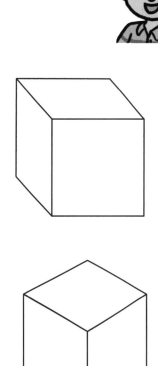

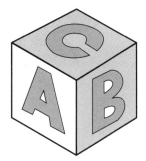 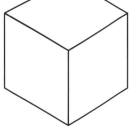

1. This is the drawing of a unit cube on a dotted paper.

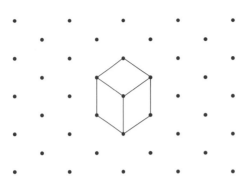

a unit cube

When another unit cube is added to it, we get:

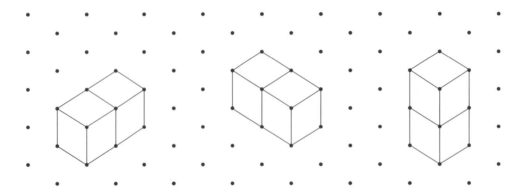

Each of these solids is made up of 2 unit cubes.

2. (a) Use 4 unit cubes to build a solid like this:

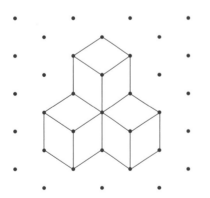

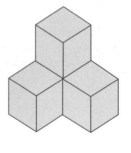

   (b) Build a different solid with 4 unit cubes.

3. Use 8 unit cubes to build a bigger cube.

Exercise 5, pages 173-174

4. Use unit cubes to build this solid.

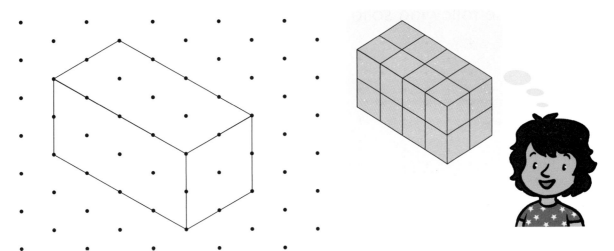

How many unit cubes are needed to build the solid?

5. Use unit cubes to build each of the following solids.

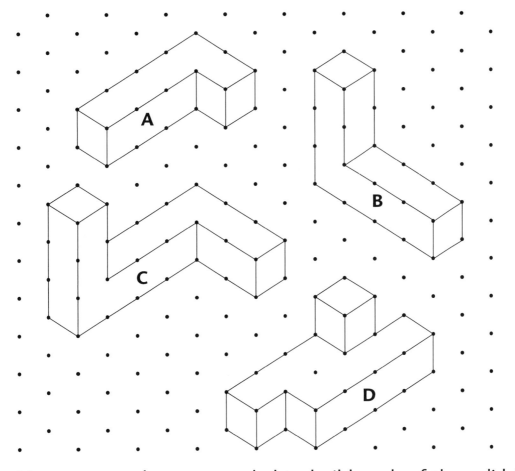

How many cubes are needed to build each of the solids?

6. How many unit cubes are needed to build each of the following solids?

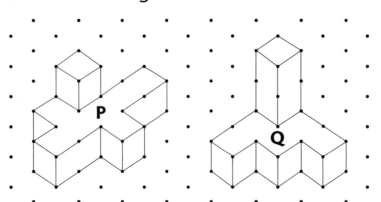

Exercise 6, pages 175-176

7. Use unit cubes to build Solid A.
Then remove some unit cubes to get Solid B.
How many cubes are removed?

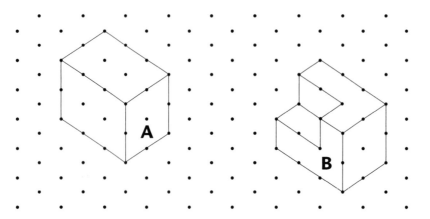

8. Use unit cubes to build Solid C.
Then add some unit cubes to get Solid D.
How many cubes are added?

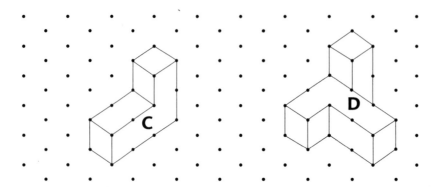

Exercise 7, pages 177-178

9.

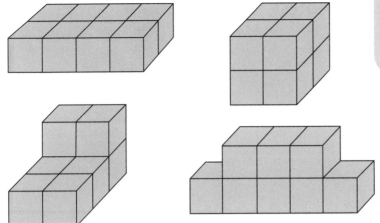

The **volume** of a solid is the amount of space it occupies.

These solids have the same volume.

The volume of each solid is cubic units.

The volume of a unit cube is **1 cubic unit**.

10. Use 6 unit cubes to build a solid like this:

Its volume is 6 cubic units.

Rearrange the 6 cubes to build another solid like this:

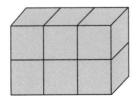

Its volume is cubic units.

11. What is the volume of each of the following solids?
    Which solid has the greatest volume?

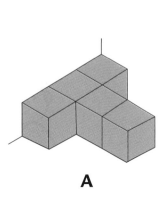

A

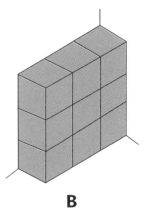

B

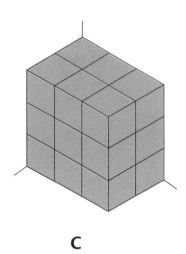

C

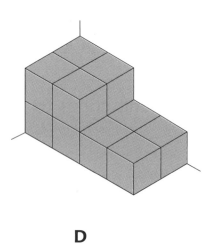

D

Exercise 8, page 179

1. Write the fractions in order, beginning with the smallest.

   (a) $\frac{5}{6}, \frac{2}{6}, \frac{3}{6}$ (b) $\frac{4}{9}, \frac{2}{3}, \frac{7}{9}$ (c) $\frac{3}{8}, \frac{3}{4}, \frac{1}{2}$

2. Fill in the blanks.

   (a) If ▲ stands for 5 people,

   ▲▲▲▲▲▲ stand for ⬚ people.

   (b) If ■■■■ stand for 40 books,

   each ■ stands for ⬚ books.

3.

   A   **B**   **C**

   (a) Which two figures have the same area?
   (b) Which two figures have the same perimeter?

4.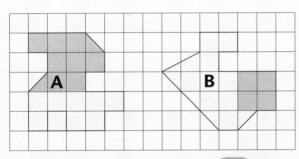

   (a) The area of Shape A is ⬚ square units.

   (b) The area of Shape B is ⬚ square units.

   (c) Which shape is bigger, A or B?

   (d) What fraction of the total square units are blue in Shape A?

   (e) What fraction of the total square units are blue in Shape B?

5. The figure shows a solid A that is made up of unit cubes. How many unit cubes are removed from Solid A to get Solid B?

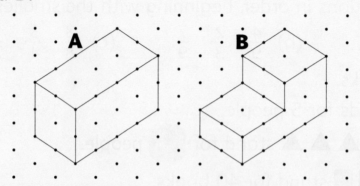

6. Solid A is made up of unit cubes.

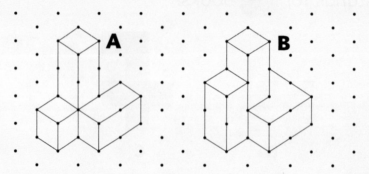

   (a) How many unit cubes are needed to build A?
   (b) How many unit cubes are added to Solid A to get Solid B?

7. This graph shows John's savings in five months.

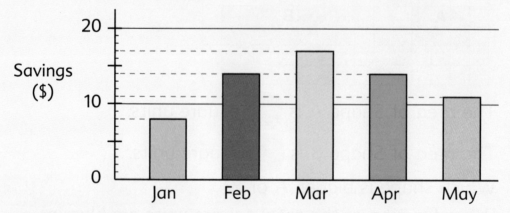

   (a) How much did John save in January?
   (b) In which month did he save the most?
   (c) Find his total savings in the 5 months.

8. The total weight of 2 bags of sugar and one bag of flour is 4 lb 2 oz.
   If the weight of each bag of sugar is 10 oz, find the weight of the bag of flour.

9. The length of a dining table is 5 ft 6 in.
   The width of the table is half that of the length.
   What is the width of the dining table in feet and inches?

10. Eric bought 7 cans of paint.
    Each can contained 1 gal of paint.
    He used 3 gal 1 qt of paint to paint his room.
    How much paint was left?

11. Which container has the most water in it?

Container A	3 pt
Container B	1 qt
Container C	7 c
Container D	half-gal

12.

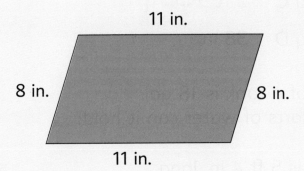

11 in.

8 in.   8 in.

11 in.

(a) Find the perimeter of this figure.
(b) How many right angles does this figure have?
(c) How many pairs of parallel sides does this figure have?
(d) Is this figure a pentagon?

13. Mrs. Jackson paid $72 for some salmon.
    The cost of the salmon was $6 per pound.
    How many pounds of salmon did Mrs. Jackson buy?

14. A bag of beans weighing 2 lb 7 oz was divided equally
    into 3 portions.
    What is the weight of each portion of beans in ounces?

15. A basket of oranges weighs 25 lb 3 oz.
    The empty basket weighs 1 lb 4 oz.
    What is the weight of the oranges?

16. A toy train is 19 in. long.
    Write the length in feet and inches.

17. Arrange the following lengths in order. Start with
    the longest.

String A	3 ft 1 in.
String B	29 in.
String C	2 ft 9 in.
String D	38 in.

18. The capacity of a tank is 18 gal.
    How many quarts of water can it hold?

19. A blue ribbon is 5 ft 4 in. long.
    A yellow ribbon is 2 ft 8 in. shorter.
    What is the total length of the blue and yellow ribbons?

20. Tyrone weighs 80 lb 10 oz.
    Juan weighs 12 oz less than Tyrone.
    Sean weighs 1 lb 8 oz more than Tyrone.
    What is the total weight of the three boys?

21. Fill in each ⬜ with 'certain', 'impossible', 'likely' or 'unlikely'.

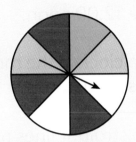

(a) It is ⬜ that the spinner will land on red or blue.

(b) It is ⬜ that the spinner will land on green, blue,
    white or red.

(c) It is ⬜ that the spinner will land on green.

(d) It is ⬜ that the spinner will land on black.

GLOSSARY

Word	Meaning
a.m.	**a.m.** is used to tell the time after 12:00 midnight and before 12:00 noon. It is eight o'clock in the morning. The time is 8:00 **a.m.**
angle	When two straight lines meet, they form an **angle.** 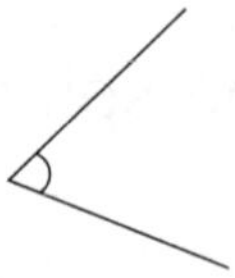
area	The **area** of a figure is the amount of flat space it covers. 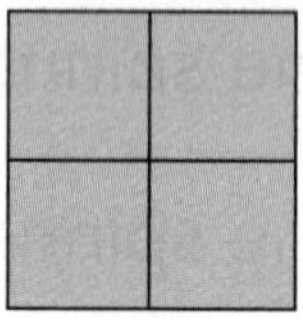 The area of the above figure is 4 square centimeters.
denominator	In the fraction $\frac{1}{2}$, '2' is the **denominator**. $\frac{1}{2}$ ◄— denominator
equilateral triangle	An **equilateral triangle** is a triangle that has three equal sides. 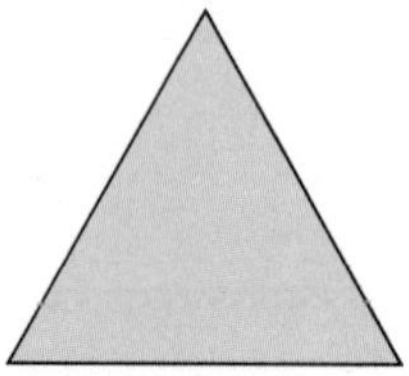

Word	Meaning
equivalent fractions	**Equivalent fractions** are different ways of writing the same fraction. $\frac{1}{3}$ and $\frac{2}{6}$ are equivalent fractions.
hexagon	A **hexagon** is a polygon with six sides.
intersect	When two straight lines **intersect**, they cross each other at one point.
isosceles triangle	An **isosceles triangle** is a triangle that has two equal sides.
kilometer	The **kilometer** is a unit of length used to measure long distances. We write **'km'** for kilometer. 1 kilometer = 1000 meters
mile	The **mile** is a unit of length used to measure long distances. We write **'mi'** for mile. 1 mile = 5280 feet

Word	Meaning
milliliter	A **milliliter** is a unit of volume. We write **'ml'** for milliliter. 1000 milliliters = 1 liter
numerator	In the fraction $\frac{1}{2}$, '1' is the **numerator**. $\frac{1}{2}$ ⟵ numerator
octagon	An **octagon** is a polygon with eight sides.
p.m.	**p.m.** is used to tell the time after 12:00 noon and before 12:00 midnight. It is eight o'clock in the evening. The time is 8:00 **p.m.**
parallel	When two straight lines are **parallel**, they do not cross each other no matter how long you extend them.
parallelogram	A **parallelogram** is a quadrilateral that has 2 pairs of sides that are parallel.

Word	Meaning
pentagon	A **pentagon** is a polygon with five sides.
perimeter	The **perimeter** of a figure is the distance around the figure. 4 cm 3 cm 3 cm The perimeter of this figure is $4 + 3 + 2 + 3 = 12$ cm 2 cm
polygon	A **polygon** is a closed figure with straight sides. This figure is a polygon. This figure is **not** a polygon.
quadrilateral	A **quadrilateral** is a polygon with four sides. Squares and rectangles are examples of quadrilaterals.

Word	Meaning
rhombus	A **rhombus** is a parallelogram that has four equal sides.
right angle	A **right angle** is the angle found in the corners of squares and rectangles.
right triangle	A **right triangle** is a triangle with a right angle.
scalene triangle	An **scalene triangle** is a triangle that has no equal sides.
second	A **second** is a unit of time. We write '**s**' for seconds. 60 seconds = 1 minute
square centimeter	A **square centimeter** is a unit of area. It is made up of a square with 1 cm sides.

Word	Meaning
square inch	A **square inch** is a unit of area. It is made up of a square with 1 in. sides.
volume	The **volume** of a solid is the amount of space it takes up. The volume of the solid is 4 cubic units.

Index